ALGAL CULTURES AND
PHYTOPLANKTON ECOLOGY

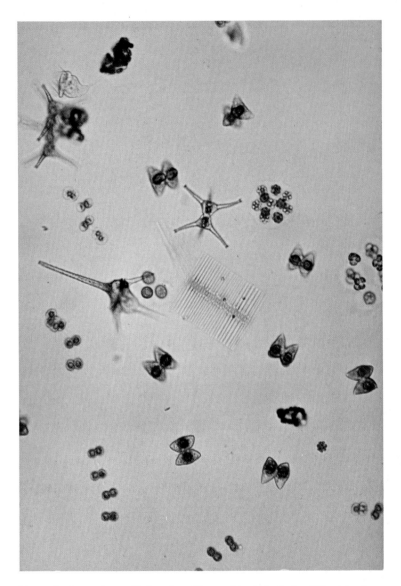

Phytoplankton from Esthwaite Water, English Lake District, June 1963; *Pandorina morum* (dividing), *Staurastrum* spp., *Fragilaria crotonensis*, *Ceratium hirundinella*, *Anabaena flos-aquae* (one colony with *Vorticella* on it), and other forms; × 170. Photograph by courtesy of Dr. H. M. Canter.

Algal Cultures and Phytoplankton Ecology

G. E. FOGG

The University of Wisconsin Press
Madison, Milwaukee, and London, 1966

Published by the University of Wisconsin Press
Box 1379, Madison, Wisconsin 53701

Copyright © 1965 by the
Regents of the University of Wisconsin

Second Printing, 1966

Printed in the United States of America
Library of Congress Catalog Card Number 64-22232

To MY WIFE

PREFACE

This book is based on a series of lectures given as Visiting Professor in Limnology in the Department of Zoology, University of Wisconsin, in the spring of 1963. While it cannot be said to present much that is new, either in outlook or factual material, the account which it gives of the applications and limitations of culture methods in the study of phytoplankton ecology may, it is hoped, be of value in the present phase of rapid expansion in limnological and oceanographical science.

I am extremely grateful to Dr. A. D. Hasler, both for his invitation to visit the University of Wisconsin and for his help and encouragement in preparing these lectures for publication. My gratitude must also be expressed to Mr. E. Paasche, for reading the typescript and making many valuable suggestions for its improvement, and to my secretary, Mrs. N. Last, for her patience in producing a legible version from a not altogether straightforward manuscript.

G. E. FOGG

Department of Botany
Westfield College
University of London
October, 1963

CONTENTS

ILLUSTRATIONS

TABLES

ALGAL CULTURES AND
PHYTOPLANKTON ECOLOGY

I

INTRODUCTION

The distribution and variations in abundance of the phytoplankton of lakes and seas are as yet difficult to account for except in vague and general terms. Since this microscopic floating plant life is the primary producer of the organic matter on which all other forms of life in any large body of water depend, the inadequacy of our knowledge, lamentable enough in itself, is reflected through the entire fields of freshwater and marine biology and on the economic plane limits the efficiency with which both fresh water and the sea can be exploited as sources of food. Undoubtedly, more extensive and detailed observations of phytoplankton populations and environmental factors in natural waters will contribute greatly to our understanding of what is taking place, but studies in the laboratory with cultures of phytoplankton algae under precisely controlled conditions also have an indispensable part to play. As in ecology generally, full understanding of the growth of organisms in their natural habitats will be achieved only by the synthesis of the results of physiological and biochemical investigations and the results of field studies. The obstacles in the way of such synthesis may perhaps be less in the study of plankton than in other branches of ecology. In the present state of our ignorance, at least, both the environment and the organisms seem of less intractable complexity than those in a terrestrial community. If this is so, it should not be too difficult to relate results obtained under the artificial conditions of the laboratory to the natural situation. Equally, attempts to carry out controlled experiments *in situ* in lakes or in the sea to discover the basic factors at work do not seem altogether futile.

It is the purpose of this book to outline the principal features of the growth of algae in culture and to discuss how far they assist in the understanding of phytoplankton ecology. Both freshwater and marine phytoplankton will be considered, for it is reasonable to suppose that the factors controlling plankton growth are basically similar in fresh and salt waters, and that, *mutatis mutandis*, the principles discovered should apply in either environment. Some discussion of phytoplankton photosynthesis is inevitable, but it is not intended to give here any extensive account of the already well-documented topic of primary productivity (for reviews see Strickland, 1960; Talling, 1961a; Steemann Nielsen, 1960, 1963; Fogg, 1963).

It will be as well to begin by emphasizing that there are many pitfalls and that we must be extremely cautious in applying results obtained with laboratory cultures to the interpretation of events in a lake or in the sea. In the first place, the algae most studied in the laboratory, predominantly species of *Chlorella*, are largely soil or non-planktonic aquatic forms. Cultures of these algae are sometimes described as planktonic, but this is merely meant to imply that the cells can be grown in free suspension under artificial conditions. The variety in physiological behavior found even in the genus *Chlorella* makes it clear that information obtained with cultures of these forms does not necessarily hold for other algae. Winokur (1948) showed that the growth characteristics of various species of *Chlorella* are diverse (some data illustrating this point are given in Table 2, page 20). The only truly planktonic strain which appears to have been studied in culture differs from most other strains of *Chlorella* in that it will apparently grow only photosynthetically and not on organic substrates in the dark (Fogg and Belcher, 1961). Algae belonging to other classes may be expected to be even more different, and the fact that few successes have thus far been obtained in growing species of planktonic algae in culture emphasizes the point that their growth requirements are not necessarily the same as those of the commonly studied kinds.

Natural waters themselves are unsatisfactory for sustained growth of algae in the laboratory, mainly because some essential nutrients are usually present in only trace amounts, their concentrations depending on dynamic equilibria which are disturbed as soon as the water is collected. Natural waters supplemented with various nutrients have been much used when the object has been only to produce algal material, precise knowledge of the conditions affecting its growth being unnecessary. The best known of such media is "Erd-Schreiber" solution, which is natural sea water supplemented with soil extract, nitrate, and phosphate. Artificial media for freshwater algae have been developed empirically, the simple solutions of a few mineral salts used by pioneers such as Benecke and Beijerinck being modified by variation in the proportions of the major nutrients and addition of trace elements, as these were discovered to be essential for healthy growth. These phases in the development of media have been summarized by Pringsheim (1946) in his book, *Pure Cultures of Algae*. The mineral requirements of phytoplankton have been reviewed by Ketchum (1954), and consideration of the rôles of individual elements will be found in the book edited by Lewin (1962).

Usually investigators have been content, when selecting a medium, to test a number of well-established recipes and use the most suitable with a minimum of modification. Only a few workers (*e.g.,* Rodhe, 1948; Krauss, 1953; Miller and Fogg, 1957) have undertaken determinations of growth in series of media in which the concentrations and proportions of the constituents were systematically varied. Generally, the criterion of the usefulness of a medium has been the final yield of algal material which the medium gives, and consequently the inorganic compositions of the most popular media bear little resemblance to those of natural waters. Chu (1942) was a pioneer among those who set out to devise media having some resemblance to those in which algae grow naturally. His highly successful medium No. 10 is comparable in composition and degree of dilution to the water of a eutrophic lake (Table 1). More recently there have been great improvements in artificial media for marine phytoplankton. These media bear a general but not necessarily close resemblance to sea water, in terms of concentrations of major ions. They also contain chelating agents to maintain adequate amounts of trace elements in solution, and organic growth factors (Provasoli *et al.*, 1957; see Table 1). Requirements for the latter are now known to be common among algae. Thiamine (vitamin B_1), cobalamin (vitamin B_{12}), and biotin are of most general importance, but some species require particular amino acids (Droop, 1962*b*; Provasoli, 1963). A rough estimate is that 70 per cent of planktonic algae require vitamin B_{12}. Droop (1961*b*, 1962*a*) has paid particular attention to the problems of chelation of trace elements, *p*H buffering, and the poising of oxidation-reduction potential, some or all of which physicochemical characteristics of a medium may be more crucial for the growth of a phytoplankton species than are the proportions of the major ions. The compositions of three modern synthetic media are given in Table 1, together with typical compositions of fresh water and sea water. Artificial media, simulating natural waters but of precisely known composition, have therefore reached a high level of sophistication. Nevertheless, we cannot assume exact correspondence. Natural waters cannot be looked on as simple solutions of mineral salts plus certain definite organic substances having chelating or growth-promoting properties. They normally contain a relatively high concentration of dissolved organic matter, an average value being about 5 mg/liter, and we know extremely little about the nature of the substances which make up this total. Undoubtedly, in chelation and in supplying organic growth factors, this dissolved organic material plays rôles which can be performed equally well by the chemically defined substances in artificial media, but it may also have other biological effects of which we are at present ignorant. An often-quoted example which indicates the importance of such unknowns is the finding of Rodhe (1948; see also Mackereth, 1953) that in artificial culture media concentrations of at least 0.040 mg/liter of phosphorus were required to sustain maximum

TABLE 1

The compositions of a typical eutrophic freshwater, seawater, and three synthetic culture media for algae (amounts expressed in mg/liter)

	Kettle Mere, Shropshire, England (Gorham, 1957)	Medium No. 10 of Chu (1942) modified by addition of iron as citrate	Monodus standard medium (Miller and Fogg, 1957)	Sea water (Goldberg, in Hill, 1963; Sverdrup et al., 1942)	Synthetic seawater medium ASP 2 (Provasoli et al., 1957)
Na	7.6	18.1	460	10,500	7,050
K	8.6	4.5	90	380	313
Ca	23.2	9.7	25	400	100
Mg	2.9	2.5	19	1,350	440
HCO_3	34.8	23.0	—	140*	—
Cl	13.9	—	45	19,000	10,400
SO_4	26.8	9.7	77	2,660	1,930
NO_3–N	0.05	6.8	280	0.001–0.60	8.2
PO_4–P	0.004	1.8	37	0.07	0.9
SiO_2	1.0	12.3	—	6.4	3.2
Fe	—	0.18†	1.1†	0.01	0.8
B	—	—	0.2	4.6	6.0
Mn	—	—	0.2	0.002	1.2
Mo	—	—	0.2	0.01	—
Co	—	—	0.02	0.0005	0.003
Cu	—	—	0.02	0.003	0.0012
Zn	—	—	0.02	0.01	0.15
tris (hydroxymethyl) aminomethane	—	—	—	—	1,000
sodium ethylenediamine tetraacetate	—	—	—	—	30
vitamin B_{12}	—	—	—	—	0.002
thiamine hydrochloride	—	—	—	—	0.5
nicotinic acid	—	—	—	—	0.1
calcium pantothenate	—	—	—	—	0.1
p-aminobenzoic acid	—	—	—	—	0.010
biotin	—	—	—	—	0.001
inositol	—	—	—	—	5
folic acid	—	—	—	—	0.002
thymine	—	—	—	—	3

* at pH 7.0
† as ferric citrate

growth rates of *Asterionella formosa,* whereas in natural lake water as little as 0.002 mg/liter sufficed. Evidently there is some factor present in lake water which enables *A. formosa* to make use of extremely low concentrations of phosphate, but what the nature of this factor is remains unknown. We are also unable at present to account for the difference between the "good" and "bad" sea waters studied by Wilson (Wilson and Armstrong, 1958). Johnston (1963*b*) found that such difference persists even after supplementation with phosphate, nitrate, silicate, trace metals, chelating materials, vitamin B_{12}, and thiamine. He concluded that one or more unknown labile factors are important in sea water.

It must also be recognized that enclosing a culture in a container itself introduces differences which may be significant. The surface presented by the vessel, relative to the volume of medium, is vastly in excess of that presented by the normal amount of particulate matter in a natural water. No surface can be totally inert but must modify conditions to some extent by adsorption of solutes from the medium, if not by release of traces of soluble matter as well. It is well established that development of bacteria in water samples is proportional to the surface area presented by the containing vessel (ZoBell, 1946), so that we may expect the relationship between these microorganisms and the phytoplankton to be altered in culture. Furthermore, the small-scale turbulence patterns, which are so important for the supply of nutrients to the cells (see p. 76), are likely to be rather different in a culture vessel from those in open water. That these patterns can be critical for the survival of all but the most robust of algae is illustrated by the findings of Fogg and Than-Tun (1960) that the growth of *Anabaena cylindrica* was doubled when culture flasks were shaken at 90 instead of 65 oscillations per minute and entirely prevented at 140 oscillations per minute.

The initial objective of the laboratory worker is usually to isolate a phytoplankton organism in pure (or *axenic*) culture. This is commonly a difficult task and is perhaps achieved far less often than is claimed, since it is impossible to prove a negative; tests for the presence of bacteria, even if rigorous, may fail to demonstrate kinds with unusual nutritional requirements. Clearly, it is necessary to eliminate other microorganisms from cultures if one is to study the nutrition and metabolism of a particular species, but then the problem arises as to how far information thus gained is applicable to natural conditions in which the species is associated and interacting with others. It is apparent that there are close interrelations between plankton algae and their associated bacteria. Thus, *Asterionella japonica* was found to grow satisfactorily in culture as long as bacteria were present but ceased to grow when these were eliminated, even though a variety of possible organic growth factors was provided (Kain and Fogg, 1958). Johnston (1963*b*) found that whereas bacteria-free *Skeletonema costatum* grew poorly in various samples of sea water enriched with nitrate, phosphate, silicate, and chelated trace metals, it grew distinctly better in the same media if bacteria were present. This effect seemed largely due to production of vitamin B_{12} by the bacteria. It seems that, having studied pure cultures, physiologists and biochemists must next investigate cultures containing more than one species. Such cultures, however, are difficult to achieve. Although two phytoplankton species may apparently coexist in equilibrium in a natural water, almost invariably one will completely outgrow the other if brought into culture.

Finally it should be pointed out that the physical environment in which cultures are maintained in the laboratory does not correspond to that in which phytoplankton grows naturally. Temperature conditions need not be widely different, since temperatures in large bodies of water are comparatively stable. Laboratory cultures are customarily incubated at constant temperature although the temperature is often considerably higher than that which algae normally encounter in their original habitat, since constant temperatures above room temperature are easier to achieve. Underwater illumination, on the other hand, is extremely difficult to imitate. Gradients in intensity of total radiation can be paralleled fairly well by use of suitable neutral filters, but light quality is difficult to match. The spectral composition of light penetrating the water changes with depth, is different for different kinds of water, and varies according to the weather. Except at the immediate surface it is very different from ordinary sunlight, and it is difficult to duplicate even approximately with artificial sources (Jitts *et al.*, 1964). Since the quantum efficiency of photosynthesis varies with wavelength, and since the action spectra for various photochemical effects are different, these discrepancies cannot be ignored. In addition, natural light fields have a diurnal rhythm of variation both in quality and in quantity. Laboratory cultures are commonly incubated in continuous illumination. The inadequacies of this practice for forms such as *Hydrodictyon*, which, as Pirson (1957) has shown, requires regular alternation of light and dark if it is to survive, are obvious, but it is likely that many subtle modifications of growth and metabolism induced by continuous illumination have as yet escaped notice. Alternation of periods of light of fixed quality and intensity with periods of complete darkness may be an approximation to natural conditions sufficient for many purposes, but incubation of cultures *in situ* in the sea or lakes, inconvenient though it is, is perhaps a method that ought to be used more frequently.

II

THE CHARACTERISTICS OF ALGAL GROWTH
IN CULTURES OF LIMITED VOLUME

A general account of the laboratory culture of algae has been given by Myers (1962). The most usual kind of culture in experimental work is one in which a limited volume of medium containing the necessary inorganic and organic nutrients is inoculated with a relatively small number of cells and then exposed to suitable conditions of light, temperature, and aeration. Increase in cell numbers in such a culture follows a characteristic pattern, represented in Figure 1, in which the following phases may usually be recognized: (1) a lag or induction phase, in which no increase in cell numbers occurs; (2) an exponential phase, in which cell multiplication is rapid and numbers increase in geometric progression; (3) a phase of declining relative growth; (4) a phase in which cell numbers remain more or less stationary; and (5) a death phase. Sometimes one or more of these phases may be so curtailed as to be scarcely recognizable.

A lag in cell multiplication may be apparent rather than real if a large proportion of the cells inoculated is not viable. Cell numbers will then remain nearly stationary until the progeny of the cells capable of dividing reach a number comparable with the total inoculated (Fig. 2). This has been shown to be the most important cause of the lag when *Monodus subterraneus*

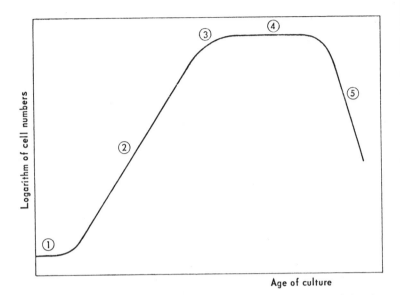

Figure 1.—The characteristic pattern of growth shown by a unicellular alga in a culture of limited volume; (1) lag phase, (2) exponential phase, (3) phase of declining relative growth rate, (4) stationary phase, (5) death phase.

is subcultured after a period of dark incubation (Belcher and Miller, 1960). On the other hand, a majority of the cells inoculated may be viable but not in a condition to divide immediately. Especially if the parent culture was an old one, enzymes may have been inactivated, and concentrations of metabolites may have decreased to a level insufficient for cell division, so that a period of reconstitution is necessary before active growth can begin. This gives rise to a true lag phase, which, of course, may be superimposed on an apparent lag due to nonviable cells. It may be noted that synthesis of cell material does not necessarily show a lag and that cells may increase in size during the lag phase.

Much of Hinshelwood's (1946) discussion of the kinetics of bacterial lag phase is of general application to other organisms and the reader is referred to his book for mathematical formulation of the relations described below for algae. The most detailed study of the lag phase in algae appears to be that on *Phaeodactylum tricornutum* (*Nitzschia closterium* forma *minutissima*) by Spencer (1954). With this species, as with *Anabaena cylindrica* (Fogg, 1944) and probably with all algae, the length of the lag was dependent on the age of the inoculum, diminishing as this entered the exponential phase of growth, being zero if the inoculum had been growing exponentially, then increasing according to the duration of the stationary phase (Fig. 3). This fits in with the picture of the lag phase as a period of restoration of enzyme and substrate concentrations to the levels necessary for rapid growth. It is to be noticed that cells subcultured during the early part of the exponential phase showed a short lag. If small inocula were used, even cells taken when exponential growth was well established showed a lag in fresh

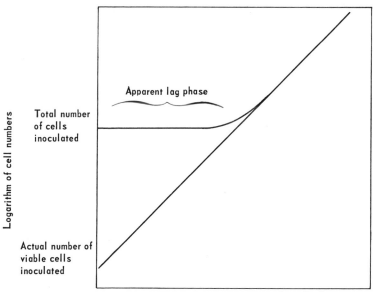

Figure 2.—Production of an apparent lag phase as a result of a high proportion of the cells inoculated being non-viable.

medium. A presumably related finding is that cultures of certain planktonic blue-green algae can be established only from large inocula (Gerloff, *et al.*, 1950). Taken in conjunction with the fact that under some conditions cells inoculated into re-enriched medium from an old culture showed less lag than similar cells in fresh medium, these results suggest that some diffusible factor

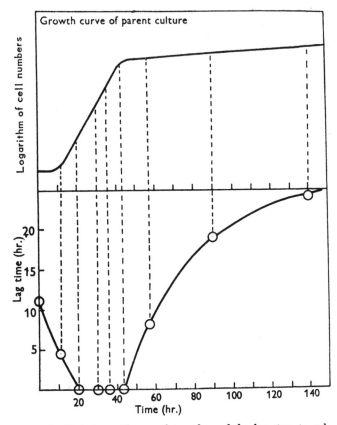

Figure 3.—Variation with age of inoculum of the lag time in cultures of *Phaeodactylum tricornutum* grown at 19° C with continuous illumination and aeration. After C. P. Spencer, Studies on the Culture of a Marine Diatom, *J. Mar. biol. Ass. U.K.* (1954), 33:285, fig. 14 (Cambridge University Press).

produced by the cells themselves is necessary for optimum growth. An alternative explanation is that some toxic factor present in the medium is inactivated by the metabolic activity of the cells. It is well established that the former state of affairs occurs with certain bacteria. Both *Bacterium lactis-aerogenes* and *pneumococci* require a certain minimum concentration of carbon dioxide in the medium for growth. In fresh medium there is a lag until this concentration is built up by respiration, but if air free of carbon dioxide is blown through the culture, the lag is prolonged indefinitely (for references see Hinshelwood, 1946).

It is possible that for some plankton algae glycolic acid, $CH_2OH \cdot COOH$, is a diffusible factor that must be built up to a certain concentration in the medium before growth can begin. Tolbert and Zill (1956) found that in short-term photosynthesis experiments using C^{14}-labeled bicarbonate, relatively considerable amounts of labeled glycolic acid were liberated by *Chlorella*. This observation has been amply confirmed, and it appears that glycolic acid is derived from ribulose diphosphate, the carbon dioxide acceptor in the photosynthetic fixation cycle, production of glycolic acid being increased at low carbon dioxide concentrations or when inhibitors of its further metabolism are present (Whittingham and Pritchard, 1963). It has further been shown (Nalewajko *et al.*, 1963) that there is rapid equilibration between intra- and extracellular glycolate. This suggests that when photosynthesis begins in fresh medium there must first of all be a lag while an equilibrium concentration of glycolic acid is established in the medium, and that only when this is achieved can the products of carbon fixation become available for growth. This idea is supported by the finding that the lag shown by small inocula of a planktonic strain of *C. pyrenoidosa* at limiting light intensities is abolished by the addition to the medium of concentrations of glycolic acid of the order of 1 mg/liter. Equivalent additions of glucose or of other organic acids do not have a similar effect. At saturating light intensities or with heavy inocula the lag phase of this strain of *Chlorella* is much reduced, as under these conditions the cells are able to establish the necessary concentration of extracellular gly-

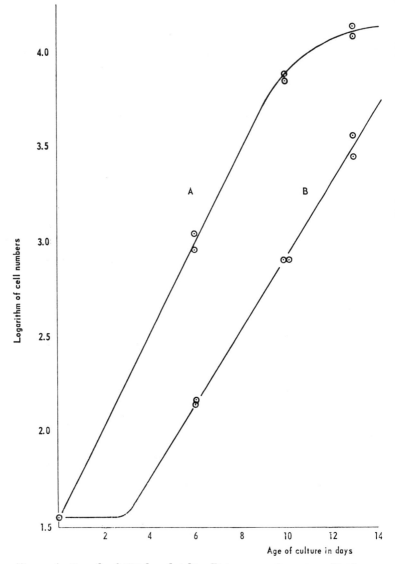

Figure 4.—Growth of *Ditylum brightwelli* in pure culture in artificial sea-water medium (ASP 2, Table 1, diluted with an equal volume of distilled water) at 18° C and 3,000 lux. *A* with, and *B* without, 1 mg/liter of glycolic acid, both adjusted to *p*H 7.5. Unpublished data of Paredes.

colic acid rapidly (Nalewajko *et al.*, 1963). A similar elimination of the lag phase by low concentrations of glycolic acid has been found by Paredes (unpublished) with *Ditylum brightwelli* in pure culture (Fig. 4). Another marine plankton form, *Micromonas squamata*, did not, however, show this effect.

A lag phase may also be exhibited when algal cells are subcultured into medium containing high concentrations of some particular substance. Spencer (1954) found that *Phaeodactylum* cells from old phosphate-deficient cultures subcultured into fresh medium with increased phosphate concentration showed a much increased lag phase as compared with that of similar cells introduced into medium with low phosphate concentration. Prolonged lag phases have been observed when *Anacystis nidulans* is inoculated into media containing sublethal concentrations of antibiotics (Fig. 5). Such lag phases may represent the period needed for the reconstitution of enzymic constituents of the cells to meet the changed metabolic circumstances (Hinshelwood, 1946) or, as is probably the case for the adaptation of *Anacystis* to antibiotics, the period needed for the multiplication of a rare mutant form (Kumar, 1964).

During the exponential phase, growth results in the production of more material, which is itself capable of growth, so that the actual rate of growth accelerates continuously. This can be represented by the expression

$$W = W_o e^{kt},$$

in which W_o is the total amount of cell material in the culture at zero time, W the amount after a period of time, t, e the base of natural logarithms, and k (sometimes denoted by R) the relative growth constant, which is a measure of the efficiency of growth. In large populations in which cell divisions are not synchronized, increase in cell numbers (N) per unit volume takes place smoothly and may be represented by the corresponding expression:

$$N = N_o e^{kt}$$

whence

$$k = \frac{\log_e N - \log_e N_o}{t}$$

or, if logarithms to the base 10 are preferred,

$$k' = \frac{\log_{10} N - \log_{10} N_o}{t}.$$

From this, the mean doubling time G (which equals the mean generation time if the cells divide into two) will be

$$G = \frac{0.301}{k'}.$$

Values of k based on different measures of growth, such as cell numbers, volume of algal material, or cell nitrogen, must clearly

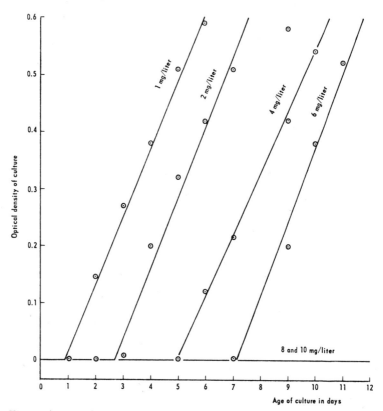

Figure 5.—Growth of *Anacystis nidulans* in the presence of different concentrations of chloramphenicol. Data of Kumar, 1964.

be approximately the same but need not be identical, since the mean generation time may remain constant while the mean cell volume or dry weight diminishes.

Values for the relative growth constant and mean doubling times for various planktonic and non-planktonic algae are given in Table 2. Measured under standard conditions, k' is usually rather constant for a particular species. Its value may depend on a variety of physiological and metabolic factors, but size is generally of most importance, since it determines the surface/volume ratio and thus the relative rate at which materials for growth can be taken into the cell. It is a general observation that small species grow faster than large ones. For example, in Table 2 it will be seen that the small forms, *Chlorella* and *Anacystis,* grow much more rapidly than the large ones, *Ceratium tripos* and *Coscinodiscus* sp. However, in a miscellaneous collection of species growing in a variety of different media, the relation of relative growth constant to surface/volume ratio is obscured. Belcher and Miller (1960) determined k' under standard conditions for a number of related algae. From other sources the surface/volume ratios of the same species can be calculated. Figure 6 shows that for these data there is a reasonable correlation between k' and surface/volume ratio, although the two *Tribonema* species are filamentous and the others approximately spherical. However, as Paasche (1960a) has pointed out, such a correlation may not hold for cells with large vacuoles. In such cells, that part of the cytoplasm in which photosynthesis occurs may have just as much surface available for exchange of materials as would the same volume of cytoplasm in a smaller cell lacking vacuoles.

For a given species the relative growth constant is a function of temperature, light intensity, and other environmental factors. As Table 2 shows, it increases with temperature. The Q_{10} of k is usually from 2 to 4 until unfavorably high temperatures are reached. Optimum temperatures are generally between 20° and 25° C, but the thermophilic strains of *Chlorella* and *Anacystis nidulans* grow best at about 40° C. However, optimum temperatures may vary with light intensity and concentration

TABLE 2

Relative growth constants, k', in $\log_{10}$ day units, and mean doubling times, G, in hours, of various planktonic and non-planktonic algae grown in continuous light of intensities approximately saturating for photosynthesis

Species	k'	G	Temp. ° C	Reference
Chlorophyceae				
Chlorella pyrenoidosa	0.12	60.2	10	Fogg and Belcher, 1961
planktonic strain	0.37	19.6	20	Fogg and Belcher, 1961
Chlorella pyrenoidosa	0.93	7.75	25	Sorokin, 1959
Emerson strain	0.90	8.0	25	Sorokin, 1959
7-11-05 strain	2.78	2.6	39	Sorokin, 1959
Xanthophyceae				
Monodus subterraneus	0.074	97.7	15	Fogg *et al.*, 1959
	0.191	37.8	20	Fogg *et al.*, 1959
	0.297	24.3	25	Fogg *et al.*, 1959
	0.169	42.7	30	Fogg *et al.*, 1959
Chrysophyceae				
Isochrysis galbana	0.24	30.2	20	Kain and Fogg, 1960
Cricosphaera (Syracosphaera) carterae	0.36	20.1	18	Parsons *et al.*, 1961
Bacillariophyceae				
Asterionella formosa	0.75	9.6	20	Lund, 1949
Asterionella japonica	0.52	13.9	20–25	Kain and Fogg, 1960
Phaeodactylum tricornutum	0.72	10.0	25	Spencer, 1954
Skeletonema costatum	0.55	13.1	18	Parsons *et al.*, 1961
Coscinodiscus sp.	0.20	30.0	18	Parsons *et al.*, 1961
Dinophyceae				
Amphidinium carteri	0.82	8.8	18	Parsons *et al.*, 1961
Prorocentrum micans	0.13	55.5	20	Kain and Fogg, 1960
Ceratium tripos	0.087	82.8	20	Nordli, 1957
Myxophyceae				
Anabaena cylindrica	0.68	10.6	25	Fogg, 1949
Anacystis nidulans	3.55	2.0	41	Kratz and Myers, 1955

of certain nutrients, and adaptation to higher or lower temperatures may sometimes occur. Hutner *et al.* (1957) succeeded in growing *Ochromonas malhamensis* above 35° C—the maximum temperature tolerated in the normally adequate basal medium—by supplying thiamine and vitamin B_{12} at 300 times the normal concentrations. A similar interaction between nutrient concentration and temperature has been reported by Maddux and Jones (1964). They found that the optimum temperatures for growth

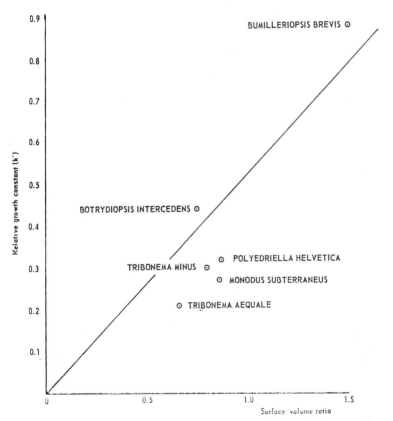

Figure 6.—Relation of relative growth constant to surface/volume ratio for six algae grown under standard conditions. Data of Belcher and Miller, 1960.

of *Nitzschia closterium* and *Tetraselmis* sp. in continuous culture were lower when a medium with nitrate and phosphate concentrations similar to those found in natural waters was used than they were when a medium having higher concentrations of these substances was employed. As would be expected, the relative growth rate bears the same general relationship to light intensity as does the rate of photosynthesis, increasing proportionately to intensity when intensity is the limiting factor and being independent of intensity when saturating values are reached. However, in the relation of growth to light intensity, there is the complication that adaptation to different intensities occurs rather quickly while exponential growth is taking place. This is well illustrated by some results obtained with *Chlorella vulgaris* by Steemann Nielsen *et al.* (1962). The alga was grown under high (30 kilolux) and low (3 kilolux) light intensity in dilute culture so that there was no appreciable shading of cells by others. The curves relating rate of photosynthesis to light intensity for the two cultures are quite different (Fig. 7), the cells grown in low light being more efficient at low intensities

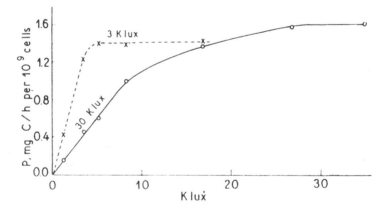

Figure 7.—The rate of photosynthesis per unit number of cells as a function of light intensity for *Chlorella vulgaris* grown at 3 or 30 kilolux. After E. Steemann Nielsen, V. K. Hansen, and E. G. Jørgensen. The adaptation to different light intensities in *Chlorella vulgaris* and time dependence on transfer to a new light intensity, *Physiol. Plant.* (1962), *15*:508, fig. 2, part *a* (Munksgaard A.S.).

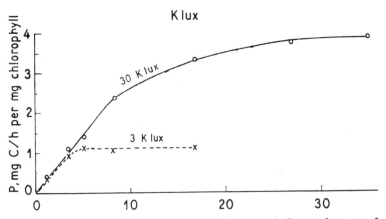

Figure 8.—The rate of photosynthesis per mg chlorophyll as a function of light intensity for *Chlorella vulgaris* grown at 3 or 30 kilolux. After E. Steemann Nielsen, V. K. Hansen, and E. G. Jørgensen. The adaptation to different light intensities in *Chlorella vulgaris* and time dependence on transfer to a new light intensity, *Physiol. Plant.* (1962), *15*:508, fig. 2, part *b* (Munksgaard A.S.).

but becoming saturated at a lower level than the cells grown in high light. The greater efficiency of the low light cells results from their higher concentration of chlorophyll, since, if photosynthesis per unit amount of chlorophyll is plotted, there is no difference between the two types when light is limiting (Fig. 8). This behavior of *Chlorella* thus corresponds to the production of "shade" and "sun" leaves by higher plants. Adaptation by the alga from one condition to the other is comparatively rapid, requiring only one division cycle, *i.e.*, about 17 hours under the experimental conditions used. The existence of such adaptation explains the discrepancy, pointed out by Myers (1951), that *Chlorella* appears to be able to produce material in photosynthesis as much as twice as fast as it can utilize it in growth. This finding was based on the comparison of curves showing the relation of relative growth rate and photosynthetic rate to light intensity. It is now realized that this comparison is not valid because the algal cells used in the two series of determinations were differently adapted. Those used in the growth determinations were grown at, and therefore adapted to, each intensity at which measurements were made, whereas those used in the photosynthesis experiment were all grown at the same intensity and were therefore not adapted to the different intensities at which rates of photosynthesis were determined (Myers, in Riley, in the press).

Many algae are able to utilize organic substrates, such as sugars and organic acids, to maintain growth in complete darkness or as the sole source or a supplementary source of carbon in the light. The algae able to grow in darkness (see the review by Danforth, 1962) are derived mainly from soil, heavily contaminated water, or littoral marine habitats (Lewin, 1963). Thus far no truly planktonic form has been reported as being capable of this. The planktonic strain of *Chlorella pyrenoidosa* has not been found able to grow in the dark, although tested with a variety of substrates under a number of different conditions (Fogg and Belcher, 1961; Nalewajko *et al.*, 1963), and a number of planktonic diatoms, including *Chaetoceros* spp. and *Skeletonema costatum* examined by Lewin (1963), have likewise been found incapable of chemotrophic growth. Pintner and Provasoli (1963) found that, although substrates such as lactate greatly stimulated the growth of the chrysomonad *Hymenomonas* sp., they did not support growth in the dark. Nevertheless, as we shall see later (p. 65), the possibility that planktonic algae can grow in the dark must be considered. In the light an organic substrate may enable an alga to attain a higher relative growth rate than would be possible without the substrate. Roach (1928), for example, found that *Scenedesmus costulatus* var. *chlorelloides* at saturating light intensities attained a maximum value for k which could not be increased by supplying glucose. At limiting light intensities, however, k was increased by a supply of glucose but never to a value more than that attained at saturating light intensity. Such enhancement of growth by glucose occurs also with the planktonic *C. pyrenoidosa* (Fogg and Belcher, 1961). Provision of organic substrates may increase growth at saturating light intensities by acting as an alternative source of carbon if the concentration of carbon dioxide is not saturating. However, the growth of *Ochromonas malhamensis*, a flagellate which is capable of phagotrophic as well as chemotrophic and phototrophic nutrition, is increased by organic substrates even when light and carbon dioxide are saturating for photosynthesis (Myers and Graham, 1956). Its mean generation time, with or without light, in the presence of glucose or sucrose is about 14 hours, whereas light and carbon dioxide alone will support marginal growth with a mean generation time of about 3 days. Myers and Graham concluded that *Ochromonas* "is a very primitive animal which has retained only enough of its photosynthetic apparatus to sustain it between bites." When organic substrates are assimilated by algae in the light, it appears from the evidence of tracer studies with C^{14} that they are assimilated directly, rather than after oxidative breakdown to carbon dioxide (Fogg and Millbank, 1960). It may be noted that Pringsheim and Wiessner (1961) found this type of nutrition to be obligatory in *Chlamydobotrys* sp., which is able to grow only in the light with acetate, but not with carbon dioxide, as the carbon source.

The assimilatory mechanisms of algae appear to be saturated by extremely low concentrations of mineral ions, so that it is technically difficult to study the effects of mineral nutrient limitation on exponential growth. The effect of supplying a low concentration of a particular nutrient in a culture of limited volume is to shorten the duration of this exponential phase rather than reduce the relative growth rate. The expected relationship of relative growth constant, k, to concentration of limiting nutrient, c, is given by the following expression (Hinshelwood, 1946):

$$\frac{k}{k_\infty} = \frac{c}{c + c_1},$$

in which c_1 is a constant having the dimensions of a concentration (being numerically equal to the concentration of the nutrient giving half the maximum growth rate, k_∞). A nutrient is limiting only when c is not large compared with c_1. It follows from this relation that so long as cell numbers are sufficiently low as not to alter appreciably the concentration of the nutrient,

k remains constant during growth even though the concentration is a limiting one.

In cultures of limited volume no marked effects on k' have been found when nitrate-nitrogen concentration was varied down to 0.1 mg/liter with *Phaeodactylum tricornutum* (Spencer, 1954), between 2.8 and 0.28 mg/liter for *Monodus subterraneus* (Miller, 1957), and between 140 and 14 mg/liter for *Asterionella japonica* (Kain and Fogg, 1958).

The continuous culture technique (p. 33) offers the best means of investigating this problem; so far it has been little used in this connection in algal studies, but it may be well to anticipate here and summarize the results that are available. Myers (1947), using this method, found that with respect to relative growth rate *Chlorella pyrenoidosa* was insensitive to changes in major salt concentration involving variation in nitrate-nitrogen concentration from 340 down to 17 mg/liter. More recently, Jones (in Riley, in the press) has found a pronounced interaction of nutrient concentration and light intensity in their effects on the growth rate of *Carteria* sp. in continuous culture. At low light intensities the concentration of nutrients had no effect, but at medium light intensities, when the nitrate-nitrogen concentration was 140 mg/liter and the phosphorus concentration 15.5 mg/liter, the maximum relative growth rate was about 4 times as great as it was when 0.125 and 0.012 mg/liter, respectively, of these nutrients were supplied. Furthermore, growth took place at much higher light intensities when the nutrient concentration was at the higher level than it did when it was at the lower level.

If conditions change during exponential growth, the relative growth rate changes accordingly within a short space of time, as shown by experiments carried out by Lund (1949) with *Asterionella formosa*. Thus, the view that k is determined by conditions at the beginning of the exponential growth period, or in other words, that cells acquire a certain growth potential which determines the rate of subsequent growth irrespective of changing environmental conditions, does not appear to be correct.

It may also be noted that algae evidently possess considerable powers of adaptation to antimetabolites and antibiotics. By subculturing the blue-green alga *Anacystis nidulans* in gradually increasing concentrations of such substances as streptomycin, penicillin, chloramphenicol, sulfanilamide, and sodium selenate, Kumar (1964) has been able to produce strains resistant to their toxic effects. For example, in the course of 15 serial transfers he was able to produce a stable strain resistant to 50,000 times the concentration of streptomycin tolerated by the original strain. Such adapted strains did not show greatly reduced relative growth rates; k' for a strain resistant to 200 ppm of streptomycin and growing in medium containing that concentration was 0.347 as compared with 0.382 for the original strain in the absence of the antibiotic, both being measured at 33° C.

Sooner or later, exponential growth must cease in a culture of limited volume. The factors involved are various:

1. *Exhaustion of nutrients.* With cultures in the older types of media it is commonly the nitrate or iron supply which limits exponential growth. If this is so, then addition of further amounts of the limiting nutrient will prolong the exponential phase until some other factor becomes limiting. Unchelated ferric iron is precipitated as phosphate in alkaline medium; in this form it is largely unavailable to algae, and it is difficult to ensure that the supply is adequate. The introduction of chelating agents such as ethylenediamine tetraacetic acid (versene or EDTA) has enabled quantities of iron and other trace elements sufficient for prolonged exponential growth to be supplied in the medium without toxic effects. Algae having a requirement for organic growth factors such as vitamin B_{12} may have the period of their exponential growth limited by the supply of these factors.

2. *Rate of supply of carbon dioxide or oxygen.* In stagnant cultures in a mineral medium the rate of diffusion of carbon dioxide into the culture from the air becomes limiting at a comparatively low population density. Improvement of the rate of aeration by shaking or stirring the culture or bubbling air through it will in this case prolong exponential growth. A supply of carbon dioxide enriched air may be necessary to maintain exponential growth in dense cultures. One or 5 per cent carbon dioxide is commonly supplied to algal cultures, but concentrations as high as this may

have inhibitory effects, as, for example, with *Anabaena cylindrica* (Fogg and Than-Tun, 1960). Oxygen may similarly become limiting in heterotrophic cultures of algae, and here, again, aeration prolongs the exponential growth phase (Pearsall and Bengry, 1940).

3. *Alteration of pH of the medium as a result of preferential absorption of particular constituents of the medium.* It commonly happens that if nitrogen is supplied as an ammonium salt the preferential absorption of the ammonium ion causes the medium to become too acid to support growth. Absorption of nitrate ion results in an increase in pH but this is buffered by the medium's taking up more carbon dioxide so that it rarely affects growth to an appreciable extent. If carbon dioxide is limiting, the utilization of bicarbonate in photosynthesis may result in the pH of media rising as high as 11 or more, which may bring growth to an end. Utilization of organic acids without equivalent intake of cations may also result in the medium's becoming too alkaline for growth, as has been recorded for the colorless alga *Chilomonas* (Hutchens, 1948).

4. *Reduction of the light intensity by self-shading.* Light absorption by a *Chlorella* culture approximately follows Beer's law, the intensity of the penetrating light falling off exponentially as the path length through the algal suspension increases (Myers, 1953). This relationship is shown in Figure 9. It will be readily appreciated from the figure that, as a culture becomes dense, only the cells at the surface will receive a light intensity saturating for photosynthesis, the bulk of the culture being light-limited and, if the culture is very dense, in virtual darkness. In this situation growth is no longer determined by the size of the population but by the rate of light absorption. The growth curve therefore changes its character from exponential to linear, *i.e.*, growth becomes directly proportional to time (Myers, 1953).

5. *Autoinhibition.* There is clear evidence that certain algae produce substances toxic to themselves in the course of their metabolism and that the accumulation of these may eventually bring exponential growth to a standstill. Such autoinhibition has been recorded for *Nostoc punctiforme* (Harder, 1917), a strain

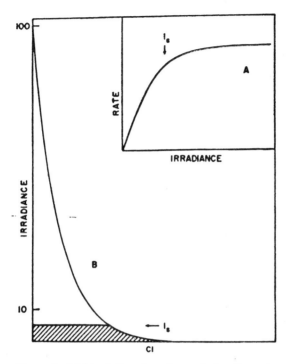

Figure 9.—Light relations in a dense algal culture. *A*, the relation of rate of photosynthesis to irradiance, showing I_s, the estimated minimum irradiance for light saturation. *B*, decrease in irradiance in the culture as a function of Cl, cell concentration × depth. After J. Myers and J. R. Graham. On the mass culture of algae. II. Yield as a function of cell concentration under continuous sunlight irradiance, *Plant Physiol.* (1959) *34*:346, fig. 1.

of *Chlorella vulgaris* (Pratt and Fong, 1940), and *Nitzschia palea* in impure culture (von Denffer, 1948; Jørgensen, 1956), but the substances concerned have not been fully characterized.

Since the changes which eventually bring exponential growth to a standstill begin as soon as a culture has been inoculated, it may occasion surprise that a protracted period of constant relative growth is ever possible. However, the changes in light intensity and in nutrient concentration brought about by growth are at first relatively small, and light and nutrients are normally supplied well above the limiting levels. From the nature of exponential growth it follows that the absolute amount of growth in any mean generation time is equal to the total of that in the period, however long, which has gone before. Hence, the reduction of the concentration of a nutrient from a level saturating for growth to zero is abrupt, and a gradual reduction in the relative rate of growth is consequently not manifest. Conversely, the production of an autoinhibitor is usually proportional to growth, so that its concentration remains at an innocuous level for a long period before suddenly mounting to the inhibitory level.

The duration of the period of declining relative growth depends on the nature of the limiting factor. Nutrient exhaustion or autoinhibition usually results in an abrupt transition from the exponential to the stationary phase, but, as already explained, if light is limiting, a prolonged phase of linear growth may intervene. Gaseous diffusion in stagnant culture is likewise dependent on the surface presented by the culture and, if limiting, produces a phase of linear growth as found, for example, in chemotrophic cultures of *Chlorella* by Pearsall and Bengry (1940).

The final yield attained in the stationary phase depends on the nature of the limiting factor. If a nutrient is limiting, it is to be expected that the yield will be proportional to the amount supplied initially. This is the basis of the use of algae for the biological assay of substances such as vitamin B_{12} (see the review by Belser, 1963). Graded amounts of a standard solution of the vitamin are added to a medium which is known to support good growth of the test organism when supplemented with the vitamin. A parallel series of culture media with graded additions of the material to be assayed is also prepared. The cultures are inoculated with an organism having a specific requirement for the vitamin, *e.g.*, with *Euglena gracilis* or *Ochromonas malhamensis* when vitamin B_{12} is being determined, and population density is measured photometrically when the stationary phase is reached. From comparison of the response curves for the standard and the unknown, the concentration of the vitamin in the unknown may be estimated. Figure 10 shows

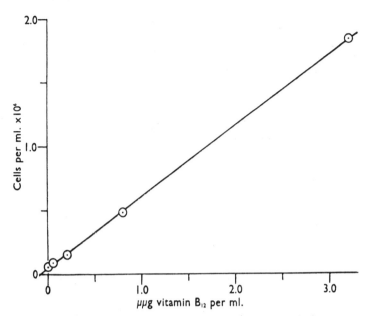

Figure 10.—Relation of final yield of cells of *Monochrysis lutheri* to concentration of vitamin B$_{12}$ in the medium. Cultures incubated at 15° C in a light intensity of 2,000 lux. From M. Droop, Vitamin B$_{12}$ and Marine Ecology: the Response of *Monochrysis lutheri*, *J. Mar. biol. Ass. U.K.* (1961), *41*:73, fig. 3 (Cambridge University Press).

a response curve for the marine flagellate *Monochrysis lutheri.* There is a linear relationship between final yield and vitamin B$_{12}$ concentration up to 3 µg/liter (Droop, 1961a).

If autoinhibition has occurred, growth will finally cease when a particular concentration of cells is reached. In this case growth is resumed if the culture is simply diluted without further addition of nutrients.

By avoiding carbon, nitrogen, and iron deficiencies and ensuring maximum efficiency of light utilization by exposing the alga in layers of only 6 mm thickness, Myers *et al.* (1951) succeeded in obtaining cultures of *Chlorella pyrenoidosa* with the extraordinarily high density of 54.9 gm dry weight of algal material per liter, or, in other terms, 25 per cent of the volume was occupied by algal cells.

Little can be said about the death phase. The time of its onset varies enormously according to species and the conditions of culture; often the stationary phase may be maintained for several weeks, but sometimes numbers may decline catastrophically immediately at the end of the exponential phase. This is so in cultures of *Ochromonas danica*, which normally show no stationary phase (Allen *et al.*, 1960). Lund (1959) has observed that illumination in the absence of sufficient amounts of certain nutrients results in breakdown of cellular organization and death in *Asterionella*. In bacterial cultures death normally follows an exponential course, the number of living cells, N_2, at time t_2 being related to the number N, at time t, by the expression

$$N_2 = N_1 e^{-k(t_2 - t_1)}.$$

Belcher and Miller (1960) found that the number of viable cells of *Monodus subterraneus* decreased in this way during incubation in the dark, and most simple algae probably show similar behavior.

A concluding comment in this chapter perhaps should be that there is no single criterion by which growth may be measured. The relative growth constant, k, the rate of growth in the linear phase, and the final yield are all useful measures but have different physiological and ecological significance and are affected differently by varying conditions. Miller and Fogg (1958) showed that the optimum concentrations and ratio of monovalent and divalent ions in the medium for exponential growth of *Monodus subterraneus* were different from those for final yield.

III

THE GROWTH OF ALGAE IN CONTINUOUS
AND SYNCHRONOUS CULTURE

Fo r many experimental purposes
cultures of limited volume are decidedly unsatisfactory. Although conditions in cultures of this type may remain sufficiently
the same to permit several days of constant relative growth,
nevertheless, they are changing, and consequently growth is
rarely "balanced," *i.e.*, attributes of the cells, such as mean size
and composition, do not remain constant. Furthermore, any
sample of the population will include cells in all stages of the
division cycle, so that measurements made on it represent mean
values, which give no clue as to the fluctuations that may be
occurring during the growth and reproduction of the individual
cells.

The method of continuous culture has been devised to over-
come the first of these two difficulties by stabilizing the environmental conditions. Continuous culture consists essentially of
holding a culture at some chosen point on its growth curve by
the regulated addition of fresh medium. This can be done in a
crude way by pouring off half of a culture after a period equal
to the mean doubling time and making up the volume with fresh
medium. A few workers, for example, Aach (1952), have used
this method, but obviously conditions in the culture may vary
considerably in the time between the additions of medium, and

unless the estimation of mean doubling time is accurate, it is difficult to hold the population at the desired level.

Automatic continuous culture methods enable precise and continuous control of population density. Of the two different types of apparatus available, the "turbidostat," which was introduced by Myers and Clark (1944), has been most used in algal studies. In this apparatus, dilution is controlled by a photometric device to keep the population density, *i.e.*, the turbidity, of the culture constant and thus balance the rate of growth. In its original form the culture vessel consists of three concentric glass tubes, the outer pair providing a water jacket, the culture being held between the inner pair, with the space in the center being occupied by one of a pair of photocells (Fig. 11). Illumination is provided by fluorescent tubes arranged so that incident light is effectively independent of the volume of the culture. Filtered carbon dioxide enriched air bubbled through the culture serves to keep the cells in suspension. The second photocell faces the same light source as the other and is balanced against it by a neutral filter. Increased density of the culture throws the photocells out of balance and results in the opening of a solenoid valve to admit fresh medium. The culture can be maintained uncontaminated for two or three months, and portions are harvested manually at suitable intervals. Once a steady state is established, the conditions affecting growth remain constant: since the cell density remains constant, the average light intensity in the culture does so also; nutrient concentrations are maintained by the inflow of fresh medium, and products of metabolism accumulating in the medium are at the same time continually diluted.

Another apparatus employing the same principle has been described by Phillips and Myers (1954). This has a constant level overflow and has the advantages that it is easier to use and enables more precise measurement of relative growth rates. Jones (in Riley, in the press; Maddux and Jones, 1964) has devised a simpler apparatus with a long light path that permits continuous culture with as few as 28 cells of *Porphyridium cruentum* per mm^3 in suspension.

In the turbidostat type of culture, growth is not limited by

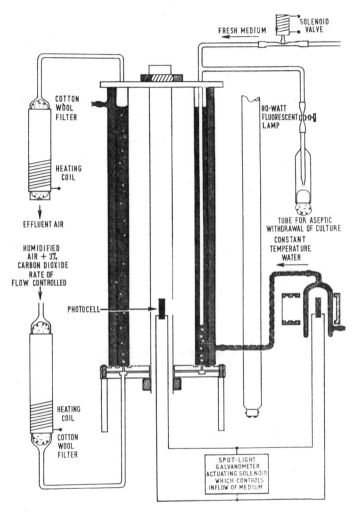

SOLENOID VALVE

FRESH MEDIUM

COTTON WOOL FILTER

HEATING COIL

EFFLUENT AIR

HUMIDIFIED AIR + 3% CARBON DIOXIDE RATE OF FLOW CONTROLLED

PHOTOCELL

HEATING COIL

COTTON WOOL FILTER

80-WATT FLUORESCENT LAMP

TUBE FOR ASEPTIC WITHDRAWAL OF CULTURE

CONSTANT TEMPERATURE WATER

SPOT-LIGHT GALVANOMETER ACTUATING SOLENOID WHICH CONTROLS INFLOW OF MEDIUM

NOT DRAWN TO SCALE

Figure 11.—A diagrammatic cross section showing the general layout of a continuous culture apparatus operating on the turbidostat principle. Modified design after Myers and Clark, 1944.

any nutrient but by factors intrinsic to the alga at the particular light intensity and temperature being used. The relative growth constant is given by an expression analogous to that which describes exponential growth in a culture of limited volume:

$$k' = \frac{\log_{10} V_t - \log_{10} V_o}{t},$$

where V_t and V_o are the total culture volumes at the end and beginning of the period of time, t. The cell populations produced have rather constant characteristics. For *Chlorella pyrenoidosa* grown at 25° C, samples taken at intervals over a period of three weeks had a mean value of k' of 0.564, with a maximum variation of 0.023, *i.e.*, about 4 per cent. Maximum apparent rate of photosynthesis was 0.687 mm³ of oxygen per minute per mm³ of cells, with a maximum variation of 0.05, *i.e.*, about 7 per cent (Myers and Clark, 1944). These variations are extremely small compared with those which occur during the course of growth in culture of limited volume.

Some results obtained using the turbidostat culture method have already been mentioned (p. 26). Myers and his collaborators (Myers, 1946a, 1946b; Phillips and Myers, 1954) have applied the technique in studies of the relation of photosynthetic and cellular characteristics of *Chlorella pyrenoidosa* to light intensity, but otherwise it has not yet been used as extensively as one would wish. It has been shown to be successful for the culture of species of *Chlorella, Scenedesmus, Euglena, Anabaena,* and *Anacystis* (Myers, 1962); *Monodus* (Miller and Fogg, 1957); *Porphyridium* (Jones, in Riley, in the press); and *Nitzschia closterium* and *Tetraselmis* sp. (Maddux and Jones, 1964).

The other kind of continuous culture device, the "chemostat" (Monod, 1950; Novick and Szilard, 1950), has been used most extensively in the study of bacterial growth. It depends on the addition of fresh medium to the culture at a constant rate, the population density then adjusting itself to a maximum rate determined by the rate of supply of the limiting nutrient. Constant volume is maintained by an overflow device. In this type of culture, a steady state is attained only if growth is limited by low light intensity or by the rate of supply of a nutrient so that the relative growth rate must always be less than the maximum possible. Fujimoto and his collaborators (1956) have grown *Chlorella ellipsoidea* by this method and have determined the relation of the limiting value of flow rate to light intensity. Clearly, this technique would be useful in the study of the effects of nutrient deficiency on the growth and metabolism of algae, but as yet it does not appear to have been used for this purpose.

It is the aim of the method of synchronous culture to produce populations of cells uniform with respect to stage reached in the division cycle. The average properties of such populations are taken as representing the properties of individual cells as they grow in size and divide. This is a more satisfactory way to study the biochemical changes involved than making observations on individual cells. Techniques do exist for measuring the respiration rate, nucleic acid content, and various other attributes of individual cells, but these are generally difficult to apply and limited in scope.

Maaløe (1962), who has given a useful discussion of the rationale of synchronous culture with special reference to bacteria, has distinguished three types of technique: (1) initial treatments, (2) repeated stimulus or entrainment methods, (3) mechanical selection procedures. Tamiya, one of the pioneers in the field of synchronous cultures of microorganisms, at first used the third of these methods. By differential centrifugation he was able to separate two categories of cells primarily distinguished by size,* which he termed "dark" and "light" cells, from cultures of *Chlorella ellipsoidea* (Tamiya *et al.*, 1953). These cells had quite distinct characteristics, as shown in Table 3. In particular there was a contrast between the high photosynthetic and low respiratory activity of the "dark" cells and the low photosynthetic and high respiratory activity of the "light" cells. By incubation of populations of these cells, the transformation of one type into the other could be followed. The principal features of the transformation of "light" into "dark" cells in

---

* It may be noted that an extremely simple sedimentation method for separating these two kinds of *Chlorella* cells for starting synchronous cultures has been described by Spektorov and Lin'kova (1962).

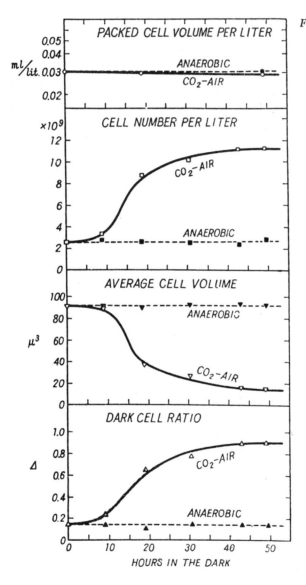

Figure 12.—Change in packed cell volume, cell number, average cell volume, and dark cell ratio during the transformation of L cells of *Chlorella ellipsoidea* into D cells under aerobic and anaerobic conditions. Reproduced from H. Tamiya, T. Iwanura, K. Shibata, E. Hase, and T. Nihei, Correlation between photosynthesis and light-independent metabolism in the growth of *Chlorella*, *Biochim. Biophys. Acta* (1953), 12:30, fig. 6 (Elsevier).

TABLE 3

Characteristics of "dark" and "light" cells of *Chlorella ellipsoidea* (from Tamiya *et al.*, 1953)

Cell type	Average cell diam. (μ)	Light-saturated photo-synthesis at 25° C	Light-limited photo-synthesis	Respiratory activity Q_{O_2} at 25° C	Chloro-phyll content (%)	Nitrogen content (%)
"Dark"	3.1 – 3.4	1.7 – 1.9	0.36 – 0.54	4.6 – 6.1	2.4 – 5.2	7.0 – 9.5
"Light"	5.5 – 5.9	0.26 – 0.32	0.10 – 0.16	7.7 – 9.3	0.8 – 1.3	5.2 – 5.7

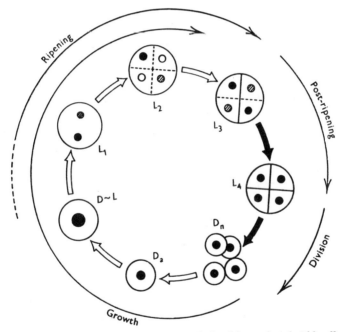

Figure 13.—Schematic representation of the life cycle of *Chlorella ellipsoidea*. The white arrows denote light-dependent processes and the black arrows transformations occurring independently of light. The black dots denote Feulgen-staining nuclei. From H. Tamiya, Cell differentiation in *Chlorella, Symp. Soc. exp. Biol.* (1963), *17*:193, fig. 4 (Cambridge University Press).

the dark are shown in Figure 12. Since photosynthesis was impossible, there was no increase in cell material, and the total cell volume remained constant. The cells divided more or less together, cell numbers increasing fourfold, then remaining stationary, while there was a corresponding fall in mean cell volume to that characteristic of "dark" cells. These changes were dependent on the presence of oxygen. The growth of "dark" into "light" cells is light-dependent but does not require the presence of oxygen. The cycle is summarized in Figure 13.

Not only does the photosynthetic activity vary during the cell division cycle but there are evidently marked changes in the nature of the products. Nihei et al. (1954) produced *Chlorella* populations consisting of 90–95 per cent "dark" cells by incubating an actively growing culture in dim light for 7 days, that is, by method 1 above. Changes in activity occurring in such a population when it was transferred to bright light and became transformed to a population of "light" cells are shown in Figure 14. The photosynthetic quotient ($\Delta O_2/-\Delta CO_2$) of "dark" cells was about unity, *i.e.*, that characteristic of carbohydrate synthesis, but rose to over 3, a value which suggests the production of highly reduced substances such as fats, when the transformation to "light" cells was complete. This supposition was borne out by elementary analyses of the cell material (Table 4).

TABLE 4

Elementary composition, in terms of percentage of dry material, of "dark" and "light" cells of *Chlorella ellipsoidea* (data of Nihei *et al.*, 1954)

Cell type	Carbon	Hydrogen	Oxygen	Nitrogen
"Dark"	39.3	6.7	37.5	8.1
"Light"	48.3	7.1	29.2	7.8

Similar variation in photosynthetic activity during the cell division cycle of *Chlorella* spp. has not been found by all investigators. Sorokin (1957) found that the photosynthetic activity of a high temperature strain of *C. pyrenoidosa* increased as the

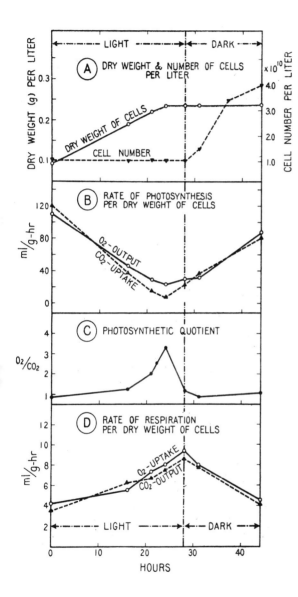

Figure 14.—Change in photosynthetic and respiratory activities during the transformation of D cells of *Chlorella ellipsoidea* into L cells. From T. Nihei, T. Sasa, S. Miyachi, K. Suzuki, and H. Tamiya, Change of photosynthetic activity of *Chlorella* cells during the course of their normal life cycle, *Archiv für Mikrobiologie* (1954), *21*:158, fig. 1 (Springer-Verlag, Berlin, Göttingen, Heidelberg).

cells grew, then declined to reach the lowest value at the time of cell division. Lorenzen (1959) found that the photosynthetic activity of another strain of the same species was fairly independent of the time of synchronous cell division, although it was affected by the light-dark changes applied. These different findings may reflect a difference between *C. ellipsoidea* and *C. pyrenoidosa* or may have arisen through the use of a different technique for synchronization. Both Sorokin and Lorenzen used continued alternation of light and dark periods, a treatment which evidently brings about synchronization by entraining the endogenous rhythm in cell division which occurs in *Chlorella* (Pirson and Lorenzen, 1958). This points to a serious uncertainty in studies with synchronous cultures, namely, that it is difficult to decide whether the observed changes are those normally accompanying the cell division cycle or whether they are induced by the treatment used to synchronize division. Perhaps mechanical selection procedures are most likely to give normal results, but if the same sequence of changes is repeated in successive cycles of synchronous division, these changes may be judged to be normally associated with growth and division. From this point of view the results of Lorenzen are perhaps the most satisfactory.

The more recent work of Tamiya and his school has been concerned largely with the biochemistry of cell division. Since this has been summarized by Hase (1962) and Tamiya (1963), it need not be discussed at length here. However, a few further points may be mentioned. The characteristics of "dark" and "light" cells, which Tamiya now prefers to call D and L cells, respectively, differ somewhat according to the previous treatment, and a great number of sub-types have been recognized (Tamiya, 1963). The effects of deficiency of certain nutrients and inhibitors on division are of some interest. In media lacking nitrate, phosphate, potassium, or magnesium, D_a cells can perform one cycle of division, giving rise to different numbers of daughter cells, which are then unable to develop normally. In a sulfur-deficient medium, however, cells grow only to the stage of early ripening (Fig. 13), then cease growing and do not divide. A similar effect is produced by antagonists of sulfur-containing amino acids, such as ethionine and allylglycine. A certain competition between growth and cell division has been observed, for L_2 cells (Fig. 13) continue to grow if kept in the light, although they are capable of limited division if transferred to the dark. It seems that protein synthesis and synthesis of specific sulfur-containing peptide-nucleotide substances necessary for cell division compete for supplies of nitrogen and sulfur. Under photosynthetic conditions protein synthesis predominates and thus cell division is prevented if these supplies are limited (Hase, 1962; Tamiya, 1963).

The most detailed work has been done with *Chlorella*. Only a few other algae have been studied in synchronous culture, and it is uncertain how far the *Chlorella* results are of general application. For references to work with other algae the review of Hoogenhout (1963) should be consulted.

IV

METABOLIC PATTERNS AND GROWTH

Fromwhat has already been said, it will have been evident that considerable variability in metabolic activity and in the products of metabolism is encountered when algae are grown in laboratory culture. Since similar variability presumably occurs in natural environments, it is important to take this into account in interpreting the behavior of phytoplankton, and it is worth considering in more detail the relation of metabolic pattern to growth.

An indication of the extent of variation possible in metabolism is given in Plate 1, which depicts young and old cultures of *Botryococcus braunii*. The young colonies show the characteristic green pigmentation of their group, the Chlorophyceae, and have sedimented to the bottom of the flask. By contrast, the colonies in the old culture, in which nitrate was exhausted, have accumulated carotenoid pigments, which completely mask the chlorophyll, and lipoids, which have lowered the specific gravity of the colonies so that they float. Equally striking quantitative differences are shown by analyses of the cell material of *Chlorella* and other algae (for references see Fogg, 1959). Those summarized in Figure 15 are for *Monodus subterraneus*. When growing exponentially, this alga has a protein content of almost 70 per cent of the dry weight, high contents of chlorophyll and nucleic acids, low contents of carbohydrate and fat, and high photosynthetic and respiratory activity. The larger cells from

Plate 1. Cultures of *Botryococcus braunii* in Chu No. 10 medium:
in the exponential phase (green) and in the stationary phase (red).
Photograph by G. E. Fogg.

an old, nitrogen-deficient culture, on the other hand, have a protein content of less than 10 per cent, low contents of chlorophyll and nucleic acids, high contents of reserve polysaccharide and fat, and extremely low photosynthetic and respiratory activity.

These, of course, are mean results for large unsynchronized populations of cells, and to some extent the differences must be due to the different proportions of cell types present at different stages in the growth of the cultures. Thus, there are certain resemblances between the characteristics of "average" cells from exponentially growing cultures and those of D cells as described by Tamiya; both are small, active in photosynthesis, and with high cell nitrogen content. There is also a resemblance between "average" cells from old cultures and Tamiya's L cells,

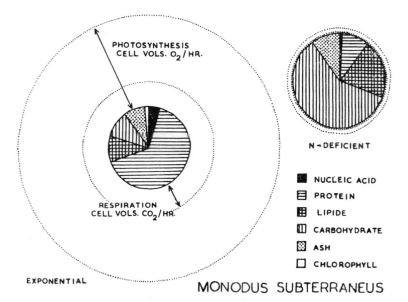

Figure 15.—Diagram showing the differences in rates of metabolism and cell composition between exponentially growing and nitrogen-deficient cells of *Monodus subterraneus*. The central areas show the relative cell diameters and compositions on a dry weight basis of the cell material. The outer annular areas are proportional to the rates of respiration and photosynthesis respectively. Data of Fogg, 1959.

both being large, inactive in photosynthesis, and low in nitrogen. However, it does not seem that the variation in average cell properties observed during the course of growth of cultures of limited volume can be entirely accounted for in terms of variation in proportions of cells in different stages of the "normal" cell cycle. There is, for example, the important difference that L cells have a high rate of respiration, whereas cells from an old culture have low respiratory activity. Furthermore, the variations during the course of growth in culture are more extreme than those which have been recorded for synchronous cultures.

There have been few studies directly concerned with the metabolism of algal cells in exponential growth, for the simple reason that the biochemist avoids the complication of increase in cell material in his experiments unless he is actually studying growth processes. It is clear, however, that exponentially growing cells of algae have high photosynthetic capacity and that the main product of their photosynthesis is protein. Efficiencies of up to 25 per cent in conversion of radiant energy into potential chemical energy have been observed in actively growing cultures of *Chlorella* (Wassink, 1954). Corresponding with the high proportion of protein found by direct analysis in such actively growing cells, the photosynthetic quotient under these conditions is greater than unity (Myers, 1949). Carbon fixed in photosynthesis is known to be incorporated rapidly into amino acids (Bassham and Calvin, 1957), and it has been found that in actively growing cells of *Navicula pelliculosa* a high proportion of carbon fixed photosynthetically appears within 30 sec in a cell fraction containing the protein (Fogg, 1956a). Protein may thus be regarded as the main and direct product of photosynthesis in this phase of growth. It may be noted that the relative rate of growth bears no direct relation to the total nitrogen content of the cells (Fogg, 1959). As with bacteria (Maaløe, 1962), it is likely that the controlling factor here is a ribonucleic acid fraction.

The effects of transferring exponentially growing cells to a medium lacking a source of assimilable nitrogen are of interest from both the physiological and the ecological points of view.

Cells treated in this way retain their high capacity for photo-synthesis for several hours, but in the absence of a nitrogen source the product must necessarily be different. The flow of carbon fixed in photosynthesis is switched from the path of protein synthesis to that leading to carbohydrate, as shown by the evidence of the photosynthetic quotient, direct analysis (for references see Fogg, 1959), and tracer experiments (Holm-Hansen *et al.*, 1959). As a result of this continued photosynthesis the dry weight of cell material in the nitrogen-starved suspension increases. Cell division takes place at first but does not continue after the cell nitrogen has fallen below a limiting value, which is generally of the order of 3 per cent of the dry weight. Thereafter continued photosynthesis results in cell expansion and increase in mean dry weight per cell.

On prolonged nitrogen starvation (Fig. 16) the maximum rate of photosynthesis of which the cells are capable diminishes, eventually becoming only 5 per cent or so of the initial rate. This is accompanied by a decrease in the chlorophyll content of the cells, but the decrease is evidently not the only cause of the impairment of photosynthetic capacity. Respiration likewise falls off but after reaching a minimum shows a rise, which may be surmised to indicate the beginning of breakdown of cell organization. From this point onwards fat begins to accumulate in the cells, which perhaps is the result of the fat-synthesizing enzyme system's being less susceptible to disorganization than is the system responsible for carbohydrate synthesis, so that the fat-synthesizing enzyme system now gets the major share of the carbon fixed in photosynthesis (Fogg, 1959).

The changes in pattern of metabolism which accompany the cessation of exponential growth in a culture of limited volume presumably depend to a large extent on the nature of the factor limiting growth. However, except for cultures in which the supply of nitrogen is limiting, there is not a great deal of information available. It cannot be assumed that the changes occurring in cultures which exhaust their nitrogen in the course of growth are necessarily similar to those just described for exponentially growing cells transferred to a medium lacking a nitrogen source.

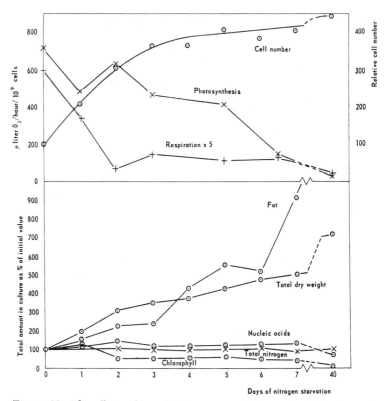

Figure 16.—The effects of transferring exponentially growing *Monodus sub-terraneus* to a medium containing no source of combined nitrogen. Data of Fogg, 1959.

In the former case the cells are subjected to falling concentrations of other nutrients and rising concentrations of by-products of metabolism as well as to nitrogen deficiency, and these may well exert their effects on the pattern of metabolism.

In ageing cultures of *Chlorella* there is a marked decrease in photosynthetic capacity. Van Oorschot (1955) found that the quantum efficiency remained constant at about 0.07 mol O_2/hv so long as nitrate was present, but that efficiency fell, when nitrogen was exhausted, to about 0.02 mol O_2/hv within 24 hours. Provided that the culture was not allowed to continue for more than a few days without a supply of nitrate, the original quantum efficiency was restored within 24 hours after addition of further nitrate. In this instance the decline in photosynthetic capacity seems directly related to exhaustion of the nitrogen supply, although Pratt (1943) found that metabolic products inhibiting photosynthesis accumulated in the medium in which another strain of *Chlorella* was grown.

Many sets of analyses (for references see Fogg, 1959) show that fat accumulates in large quantities in nitrogen-deficient cultures of Chlorophyceae, Xanthophyceae, and diatoms. Corresponding with this, the distribution of radioactivity among various cell fractions of *Navicula pelliculosa* after photosynthesis for 2 minutes in the presence of C^{14}-labeled bicarbonate has been found to be markedly different in material from old, nitrogen-deficient cultures from that in material in actively growing cultures, as much as 70 per cent entering the fat fraction in the old cultures, as contrasted with less than 20 per cent in the latter case (Fogg, 1956a). There is no evidence of a preliminary phase of carbohydrate accumulation such as is found in actively growing material abruptly transferred to nitrogen-deficient conditions. This seems explicable in terms of the different cell types which would be expected to predominate under these conditions. An actively growing population consists mostly of D cells. Nitrogen deficiency does not markedly affect the transformation of these into L cells, and the L cells produced can undergo division. The second generation of D cells, however, is unable to develop normally, and it seems that the enzymic composition of these cells may then be fixed in the state characteristic of this phase, namely, one which favors the synthesis of carbohydrates (see p. 40). On the other hand, cells in a culture in which the nitrogen supply becomes exhausted as a result of growth become arrested at the L stage, presumably as a result of the greater sensitivity of the L – D transformation to inhibitory products of metabolism under conditions of nitrogen deficiency. These cells characteristically form highly reduced products of photosynthesis (see p. 40), and fat accumulation is evidently a result of this tendency. It may be noted that actively growing

cells transferred to conditions of sulfur deficiency are halted in
the L stage, not in the D stage as with nitrogen-deprived cells,
and these accumulate fat (Otsuka, 1961).

There seems to be no particular effect of nitrogen deficiency
on the total amount of the miscellaneous fat-solvent soluble substances classed as lipoids. Collyer and Fogg (1955) found that
the proportion of this fraction in a number of species showed no
correlation with fatty acid content or inverse correlation with
cell nitrogen content.

Accumulation of carotenoid pigments, a characteristic of many
algae when growing under natural conditions, often occurs, however, in ageing cultures (Plate 1). Even if sufficient carotenoid
to make the cells bright orange or red is not produced, an increase in the carotenoid/chlorophyll ratio is usually detectable
in such cultures (Fogg, 1959). A study by Droop (1954) with
Haematococcus pluvialis showed that the accumulation of carotenoid is favored by circumstances, including phosphate deficiency as well as nitrogen deficiency, which prevent cell division
without impairing the alga's ability to assimilate carbon.

Different species of algae have a tendency to resemble each
other in the relative amounts of crude protein, fats, and hydro-
lysable polysaccharide which they contain when grown under
approximately similar conditions (Collyer and Fogg, 1955).
There may be some differences between algal classes in respect
of composition, but, with certain exceptions to be mentioned
below, these are small compared with the differences in cell
composition which a single species may show in the course of
growth in culture. Parsons *et al.* (1961) analyzed eleven different species of marine plankton representing five algal groups,
all grown under similar physical and chemical conditions and
harvested in the exponential phase. The ash content of the different species varied greatly, being especially high in the diatoms,
but if allowance is made for this by expressing the amounts of
major fractions in terms of the total organic carbon in the cells,
then the composition of the cells is generally similar (Table 5).
It will be seen that the maximum variation in protein content
here is only a little more than twofold, whereas in *Chlorella*

TABLE 5

Comparison of the cell composition of species of marine phytoplankton, grown under similar chemical and physical conditions, in terms of the ratio of components to (oxidizable) carbon (Parsons *et al.*, 1961)

	Protein/C	Carbohydrate/C	Fat/C
Chlorophyceae			
Tetraselmis maculata	1.42	0.41	0.07
Dunaliella salina	1.43	0.80	0.15
Chrysophyceae			
Monochrysis lutheri	0.94	0.59	0.22
Cricosphaera (Syracosphaera) carterae	1.41	0.45	0.12
Bacillariophyceae			
Chaetoceros sp.	1.12	0.22	0.21
Skeletonema costatum	1.38	0.79	0.17
Coscinodiscus sp.	1.08	0.27	0.11
Phaeodactylum tricornutum	0.88	0.64	0.17
Dinophyceae			
Amphidinium carteri	0.69	0.75	0.44
Exuviella sp.	0.70	0.84	0.34
Myxophyceae			
Agmenellum quadruplicatum	0.86	0.75	0.31

pyrenoidosa the variation may be more than tenfold, according to the conditions under which it is grown (Spoehr and Milner, 1949). The low value for the protein/C ratio in *Exuviella* sp. may be attributable to the thick cellulose wall which it possesses; however, a similar explanation would not account for the equally low value for *Amphidinium carteri*, the cells of which are naked.

An exception to the generalization that the gross composition of the cell material of an alga is dependent more on environmental circumstances than on class or species seems to be provided by members of the Rhodophyceae and Myxophyceae. These, unlike the algae discussed above, do not appear to accumulate fat under conditions of nitrogen deficiency (Collyer and Fogg, 1955). This may be related to the finding of Erwin and Bloch (1964) that the mechanism for biosynthesis of unsaturated fatty acids in the Rhodophyceae and Myxophyceae is different from that in the Chlorophyceae and higher plants.

Of course, algae may differ considerably in details of composition even when differences due to environmental conditions are eliminated, and it is firmly established that the various algal groups are characterized by particular pigments, carbohydrates, sterols, and other compounds.

V

THE GENERAL FEATURES OF PHYTOPLANKTON
GROWTH IN LAKES AND THE SEA

I t is quite beyond the scope of
this book to review the mass of data relating to phytoplankton
which limnologists and oceanographers have been accumulating
since quantitative observations were first begun by Hensen in
1887. In fact, much of this information is of little value for the
present purpose of describing the general patterns of phytoplankton growth and relating the salient features to the findings of laboratory studies. Techniques for quantitative estimation
of phytoplankton, a necessary prerequisite, of course, for the
accurate following of its growth, are far from satisfactory.
Details of methods are to be found in reviews such as those of
Lund and Talling (1957) and Strickland (1960), but some discussion of the chief difficulties should be given here.

Both horizontally and vertically the distribution of phytoplankton is usually patchy. The taking of samples at successive
depths is normal limnological and oceanographic practice, but
even samples taken at such relatively close intervals as one
meter may be inadequate to give an accurate estimate of abundance; divers occasionally report seeing thin horizontal laminae
of organisms, only a centimeter or so in thickness. A device,
such as a pipe (Lund and Talling, 1957), which samples the
whole of a water column, is obviously preferable from this point
of view to the usual type of water-sampling bottle. Heterogene-

ous horizontal distribution is more difficult to take into account. That blooms of phytoplankton may be extremely patchy is sometimes very obvious as one flies over coastal waters or a lake. Patches of marine plankton, which are usually elliptical in shape, vary in a continuous series from a few feet across to as much as 30 or 40 miles by 120 or 180 miles, the mean being about 10 by 40 miles. Long narrow bands or streaks, only a few feet in width, are common and may form a pattern superimposed on that of the patches (Bainbridge, 1957). In lakes, as Plate 2 shows, phytoplankton may become concentrated in streaks only five centimeters or so apart. Rodhe (1958) has shown how samples taken at a single station on a lake show, from day to day, wide fluctuations related to wind-induced water movements, highest population densities being correlated with winds blowing from the direction of the shallow, most fertile part. Clearly, many sampling stations distributed over a wide area, or some means of following and sampling a specific water mass, are needed if phytoplankton growth is to be followed under these circumstances. Verduin (1951) has compared phytoplankton data obtained by multiple mobile sampling with those from a single station, in western Lake Erie.

Much information relates to samples obtained by means of nets. This method has the obvious advantages of increasing the volume of water sampled and giving an integrated sample representing a large area. It is, however, becoming increasingly obvious that even the finest net misses an important part of the phytoplankton. Verduin (1956) measured photosynthesis in lake water before and after filtration through the finest bolting silk (64 μ apertures) and found, on the average, 65 per cent of the activity in the filtrate. Rodhe (1958) likewise found that the rate of photosynthesis in lakewater samples was more closely correlated with the numbers of nannoplankton than with the numbers of plankton retained by a plankton net. With seawater samples Holmes and Anderson (1963) found that more than half the photosynthesis was carried out by algae which passed through a net with 35 μ apertures. On the basis of direct counts, Lund (1961) estimated that "μ-algae" generally account for less

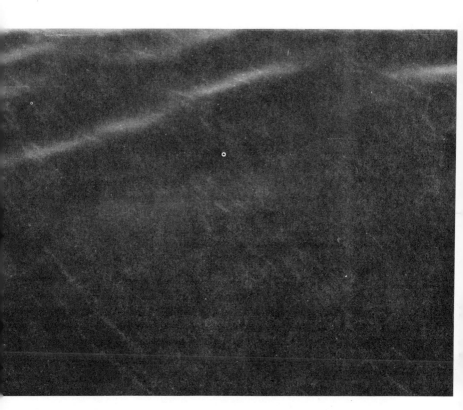

Plate 2. A bloom of *Gloeotrichia echinulata* in Lake Erken, Sweden, September 1957. The colonies have become aligned in stripes about 5 cm apart in the direction of wave movement. Photograph by G. E. Fogg.

than 10 per cent of the total algal mass in the English lakes. Evidently, as one would expect from their high surface/volume ratio, these small forms are more active per unit mass of cell material than the algae retained by a net. It is clear that net sampling is inadequate for quantitative work. Collection of large volumes of water and separation of the algae by sedimentation, centrifugation, or filtration through a fine filter seem to be the best methods. Even these are not entirely satisfactory, since certain species are extremely fragile and break up when centrifuged, filtered, or treated with chemical preservatives. For these species, a quantitative culture method seems to be the only available method at present for determining occurrence and abundance.

The total biomass of phytoplankton may be determined in terms of volume, carbon content, chlorophyll content, or various other measures. However, from what has already been said, it will be realized that the activity and growth rate of the total biomass will vary greatly, according to whether it is in the form of small or large cells and to other circumstances as well. Recognition and counting of numbers of individual species is laborious but undoubtedly provides the most useful kind of information. Given the mean dimensions of the cells, counts may be converted to volumes or to cell surface areas. Paasche (1960a) has studied the relation of rates of photosynthesis, as determined by the C^{14} method, to standing crop, expressed in terms of numbers, volumes, and cell surface area, in samples from the Norwegian Sea. As Figure 17 shows, these three measures of standing crop give strikingly different impressions of the importance of the various species. Total cell surface area was most highly correlated with rate of photosynthesis, the correlation coefficient between the two being 0.74, as compared with 0.45 and 0.62, for cell number and cell volume, respectively. Possibly, then, cell surface area is the most adequate measure of the standing stock of phytoplankton. When individual species, rather than total phytoplankton, are being studied, the various possible measures may reasonably be assumed to be sufficiently well correlated as to give equally useful pictures of abundance.

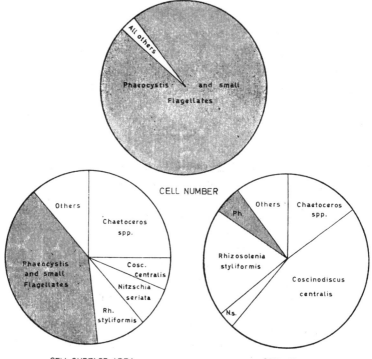

Figure 17.—Relative proportions of various species of phytoplankton from a station in the Norwegian Sea expressed in terms of cell numbers, total cell surface area, and total cell volume. From E. Paasche, On the relationship between primary production and standing stock of phytoplankton, *J. Cons. int. Explor. Mer* (1960), *26(1)*:42, fig. 6.

While these various sources of uncertainty must be borne in mind in considering details, the general features of phytoplankton growth are clear enough. There is first of all a fairly well-defined seasonal periodicity in total biomass. In temperate and polar waters, both fresh and salt, there is no appreciable growth during the winter. Phytoplankton numbers increase early in the spring, generally reaching a maximum toward the end of April. So abrupt and rapid is this increase that British biologists usually refer to it as the spring outburst. The peak is followed by an almost equally steep decline, and during the summer numbers remain at a relatively low level. A second maximum, usually not so great as the one in the spring, may occur in the autumn, after which the numbers decrease to the low winter level. This pattern is shown both by the phytoplankton as a whole (see Fig. 27) and, sometimes, by individual species such as *Asterionella* (Fig. 18).

In Arctic and Antarctic waters there is a single peak at about

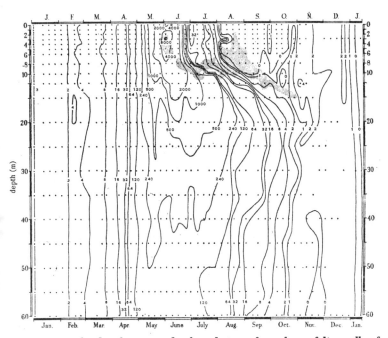

Figure 18.—The distribution in depth and time of numbers of live cells of *Asterionella formosa* per ml in Windermere, North Basin, during 1947. The dots show the depths at which samples were taken for the estimations. Isopleths (lines of equal numbers) have been drawn freehand. The stippled area shows the depth-time distribution of the greatest vertical density gradients (the pycnocline), associated with the thermocline. From J. W. G. Lund, F. J. H. Mackereth, and C. H. Mortimer, Changes in depth and time of certain chemical and physical conditions and of the standing crop of *Asterionella formosa* Hass in the north basin of Windermere in 1947, *Phil. Trans. roy. Soc.*, B (1963), 246:265, fig. 3.

mid-summer, generally similar to the spring maximum in temperate waters in its principal features. In both temperate and polar waters the seasonal amplitude in phytoplankton numbers is great, of the order of a thousandfold. By contrast, in tropical waters the seasonal variation may be as little as fivefold, and the maximum occurs in winter.

These seasonal pictures, which, of course, grade into each other, apply to most lakes and seas but may sometimes be modified by local conditions. For example, where algal production is dependent on the upwelling of cold nutrient-rich water, as in the Benguela and Peru currents, the peak in algal growth is determined by the season of upwelling. Production in tropical lakes may reach a maximum following an influx of nutrient-rich water in the rainy season.

Phytoplankton shows qualitative changes with season as well as variation in total biomass, there being a seasonal succession of species occurring fairly consistently from year to year in a given lake or area of sea. In addition, there are differences in spatial distribution, although in comparison with flowering plants phytoplankton species are characteristically cosmopolitan in distribution. For example, *Ceratium* spp. are found in all oceans, but some species are present only in particular areas. Some species are found only in warmer waters and seem to be confined to a particular region by cold water barriers (see the discussion by Steemann Nielsen, in Riley, in the press).

VI

INCREASE OF PHYTOPLANKTON
IN TEMPERATE WATERS IN THE SPRING

The spring maximum in temperate waters is perhaps the best known feature of phytoplankton development, and it is convenient to discuss the effects of most environmental factors in relation to this phenomenon. In many respects it resembles growth in a culture of limited volume. Thus it starts from a small initial number of cells in a medium comparatively rich in nutrients. It may follow an approximately exponential course for several weeks, and often a single species predominates. The final crop is sometimes roughly proportional to the initial amount of a limiting nutrient, as, for example, with *Asterionella formosa* in Windermere (p. 67).

The first problem in this course of events is the origin of the inoculum. The two principal possibilities are that a species is always present in the water, or that a species is absent from the water for substantial periods during which its resting stages are present in bottom deposits, from whence the open waters can be repopulated when conditions become favorable again. These types were distinguished by Haeckel (1890) as *holoplanktonic* and *meroplanktonic*, respectively. Good examples of both kinds are known. Lund (1949) found no evidence that appreciable numbers of *Asterionella formosa* in Windermere are derived from sheltered bays or enter by way of the inflowing streams. Resting spores of this species have never been observed. Evidently, live cells are always present in open water, and the observed increases are clearly due to multiplication in the water itself. Among marine phytoplankton *Halosphaera viridis* and *Coccolithus huxleyi* (Braarud, 1962) are examples of holoplanktonic species. It may be noted that a holoplanktonic species does not necessarily persist in a given area of sea throughout the year. *Coccolithus huxleyi*, for example, is presumed by Braarud (1962) to die off in northern and southern waters in the winter and to be re-introduced each season from warmer parts.

Melosira italica provides a clear example of a meroplanktonic freshwater alga. It produces resting stages which lie dormant in the bottom mud until conditions are favorable for their development in the water (Lund, 1954). *Cricosphaera carterae* is an extreme case of a marine meroplanktonic species, having in its life cycle a sedentary phase which may give rise to a motile phase capable of forming dense planktonic growths. *Skeletonema costatum* is a widely distributed meroplanktonic species of coastal waters which does not have a specially differentiated resting stage (Braarud, 1962). Oceanic species are characteristically holoplanktonic, whereas meroplanktonic species must be coastal in origin, although they may occur in oceanic waters if these are inoculated with coastal waters. Thus Paasche (1960*b*) attributed the abundant occurrence of the meroplanktonic species *Chaetoceros debilis* in the Norwegian Sea in 1954 to an inoculation from the Faroe region into the Atlantic water masses entering this area.

By mid-winter the concentrations of nutrients in temperate waters have reached their maximum levels. The stage has been set for algal growth, but physical conditions are limiting. Lund *et al.* (1963) found that *Asterionella* grew as vigorously in water taken from Windermere after the middle of November as it did in culture solution. Light and temperature in winter are low, but the intensity and duration of light are sufficient to support some algal growth, and abundant development of phytoplankton can frequently occur at temperatures approaching zero; development of plankton under ice is common. Nevertheless, phytoplankton numbers are generally low in winter. This is presumably because the rate of loss of whole cells, or of cell material by respiration, exceeds or approximately balances the rate of addition by growth. Increase does not become perceptible until early spring, when it begins abruptly, often showing, as with diatoms in the English lakes, a remarkably similar timing year after year.

The reasons for this abrupt beginning of population increase seem to be fairly clear. Gran and Braarud (1935) pointed out that net growth cannot occur if mixing takes place at such a rate and to such a depth that phytoplankton is carried out of the photic zone faster than it can multiply. The point at which growth exceeds depletion will be determined by both the prevailing light intensities and the vertical coefficient of eddy diffusion. The relation between the critical depth of mixing and the onset of the spring increase has been considered more precisely by Sverdrup (1953; see also Ryther, 1963). In temperate seas there is good correlation between the beginning of phytoplankton increase in the spring and the time at which the depth of the surface mixed layer becomes less than the critical depth calculated from the amount of incident radiation and the extinction coefficient of the water. A generally similar situation no doubt occurs in lakes, but other factors in addition to turbulence may operate to keep the rate of depletion of the population greater than its rate of growth. Thus Lund *et al.* (1963) consider that *Asterionella* populations in Windermere are depleted mainly by loss in the outflow, with losses from sedimentation onto the deposits, ingestion by animals, and parasitism by fungi being slight. The wetter and colder the winter, the smaller is the size of the population at the end of it.

There is no direct evidence of any event in the sequence resembling the lag phase in culture—having regard to the extremely low density of the populations concerned it is to be expected that such evidence would be difficult to obtain—but nevertheless it may be argued that something of this sort is involved. As we have already seen (p. 13), the lag phase is most pronounced in populations of low density. If a cell of a plankton alga requires a certain minimum concentration of some external metabolite in its vicinity before cell division can begin, then a dependence of increase in numbers on light intensity and decrease in turbulence, such as is observed, would be expected. The production of extracellular products is presumably dependent on photosynthesis and thus on light intensity, and if the turbulent mixing extends to the vicinity of the cells, it will delay the establishment of sufficiently high concentrations of these substances around them. It seems possible that glycolic acid is an external metabolite important in this way. Fogg and Nalewajko (1964) have found evidence that this substance is liberated from the cells of planktonic algae and that the physiological relations of this process are similar to those found in culture. Glycolic acid has been detected in lake waters in concentrations of the order of 0.2 mg/liter, but nothing is known at present of the annual cycle of variation in its concentration and its relation to the onset of growth in the spring. It may be noted here that Johnston (1963*b*) has commented that from biological assay results "poor quality has been the general rule for sea waters before the spring bloom commences. Presumably some modification of sea water must take place when light and stability become suitable, before the phytoplankton bloom is in full swing."

Increase during the spring outburst is sometimes of only one dominant species and usually follows an approximately exponential course (Fig. 19). Considering the errors of sampling and counting mentioned in the previous chapter and the fluctuations of light and temperature which occur in the natural habitat, it is not surprising that the points do not always lie along a straight line when numbers are plotted logarithmically.

It is important to note that it is not strictly correct to speak of "growth rate" in connection with natural populations of phytoplankton; "rate of increase" is better, since the same population is not necessarily being sampled all the time, and since depletion by removal or death of cells is going on concurrently with multiplication.

It will be noticed from Figure 19 that the relative rates of increase of *Asterionella* under lake conditions correspond to doubling times of 5 to 7 days. This is much longer than the time

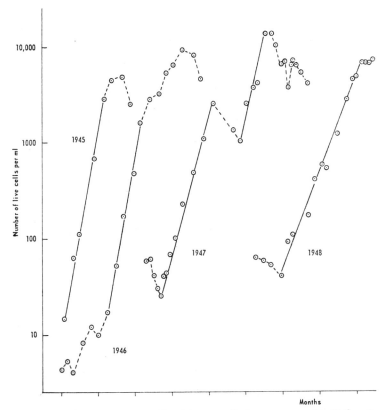

Figure 19.—Numbers of live cells of *Asterionella formosa* per ml in Esthwaite Water 1945–48, plotted logarithmically against time. Periods of approximately exponential increase are denoted by the solid straight lines. Data of Lund, 1950.

under laboratory conditions, viz., 9.6 hours at 20° C (see Table 2). This difference is mainly attributable to the fact that the bulk of the lake population is light and temperature limited, although loss of cells from the photic zone accounts for part of it (Fig. 20).

Since the depth of the photic zone is often 10 meters or less, and never more than 100 meters, the greater part of the water is usually unavailable for phototrophic growth. If chemotrophic growth of phytoplankton occurs, even at a slow rate, it might be important in contributing to the total crop, simply because, being independent of light, it could occur throughout the water column. It will be recalled from Chapter II that although many

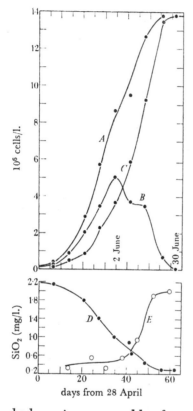

Figure 20.—Production and loss of *Asterionella formosa* in Windermere, North Basin, April 28 to June 30, 1947. The epilimnion is assumed to occupy the top 8 m, and the curves represent: A, the cumulative total of cell production computed from silicate uptake; B, the mean concentration of cells in the epilimnion (standing crop); C, the cumulative loss of cells from the epilimnion (A minus B); D, epilimnetic silicate concentration; E, relative rates of loss of cells from unit epilimnetic population (arbitrary scale). From J. W. G. Lund, F. J. H. Mackereth, and C. H. Mortimer, Changes in depth and time of certain chemical and physical conditions and of the standing crop of *Asterionella formosa* Hass in the north basin of Windermere in 1947, *Phil. Trans. roy. Soc.*, B (1963), 246:275, fig. 9.

algal species are capable of growth in the dark if given a suitable organic substrate, there seems to be no definite evidence from laboratory cultures of any truly planktonic species being able to do this. Although both fresh waters and sea waters normally contain relatively high concentrations of dissolved organic substances, the concentrations of readily assimilable substances such as sugars and amino acids are generally low. Glycolic acid may, perhaps, be a readily assimilable substrate available in quantity (Fogg and Nalewajko, 1964), and, of course, a substance present in low concentration may nevertheless have a high turnover rate and be an important energy source for growth.

Rodhe (1955) found indications of growth of nannoplankton in a sub-arctic lake during the winter under circumstances in which virtually no light could have been available. He supposed that chemotrophic growth was taking place at the expense of dissolved organic matter produced by photosynthesis during the summer. Bernard (1963) has amassed a great deal of evidence which shows that nannoplankton algae are often as numerous in samples taken from considerable depths in the sea as they are in the photic layer. It seems that chemotrophic growth must be occurring under these circumstances. Parsons and Strickland (1962) have shown by use of C^{14} as a tracer that there is definite uptake of organic substrates by natural phytoplankton populations, but it cannot be said from their results whether this is due to the algae themselves or to bacteria associated with them.

The detailed work of Lund, *et al.* (1963) showed no growth of *Asterionella* in the aphotic layers of Windermere. On the whole, however, the evidence for chemotrophic growth on the part of some phytoplankton species, at least, seems strong, though certainly far from conclusive. Phototrophic assimilation of organic substances is also a possibility that must be borne in mind (Fogg, 1963).

The factors which may operate to bring to an end this period of rapid increase in the spring are various and not necessarily the same as those which operate in cultures of limited volume. It is particularly important to remember in this connection that the population densities in cultures and in natural waters are usually of entirely different orders of magnitude. An ordinary laboratory culture of *Chlorella* may contain 10^6 cells per mm^3 when growth is complete, whereas a dense *Asterionella* bloom in Windermere has only 10 cells or so per mm^3. Even allowing for the fact that *Asterionella* cells have about 10 times the volume of *Chlorella* cells, there is an enormous difference here, and one might expect the factors controlling growth to differ accordingly.

LIGHT INTENSITY. As the concentration of cells in the water

increases, light penetration decreases, so that the phytoplankton becomes self-shading. Inverse correlations between plankton density and light penetration have been described frequently, but it is not always easy to distinguish between effects due to the plankton itself and, for example, detritus brought in by floods. Reduction of light penetration will have the same effect on growth, whatever its cause, but it is clear that chance occurrences such as floods are not usually responsible for cessation of growth, and that, if reduction of light is concerned at all, self-shading is the important factor. Talling (1960*b*) has reported a particularly clear example of self-shading by *Asterionella* in Windermere. During 1959 a well-developed peak in *Asterionella* occurred during a period of bright, calm weather with no flooding, when other plankton species were scarce. Under these conditions there was a close correlation between *Asterionella* numbers and light extinction (Fig. 21). Talling concluded that only rarely does phytoplankton reach a density sufficient to have appreciable effects in reducing light penetration. In the present context it is to be noted that the reduction in light penetration, through self-shading, while large enough to have some effect on photosynthesis and hence on growth, is not drastic. It could only account for a decrease in growth rate and not for a complete cessation in increase, such as is actually observed.

In passing it should be recorded that adaptation of phytoplankton to light intensity, similar to that found in cultures (p. 22), occurs during periods of stability of the water column (Ryther and Menzel, 1959; Steemann Nielsen and Hansen, 1959).

MINERAL NUTRIENTS. Deficiency of a mineral nutrient may be expected to be one of the most important factors causing cessation of spring growth, but clear instances of this are few. One has been provided by Lund (1950) for *Asterionella* in the English Lake District. Detailed records of the numbers of this diatom and of the levels of various environmental factors during the spring period have been accumulated over many years. Factors such as light intensity, temperature, grazing by zooplankton, and parasitism did not seem to be responsible for the cessation of growth, and, in particular, there was no correlation

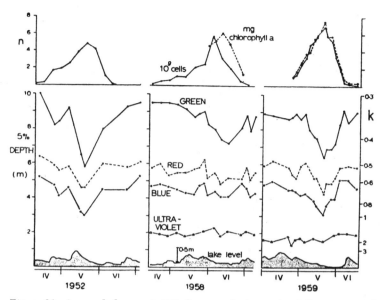

Figure 21.—Seasonal changes in Windermere, during parts of three years, of (a) numbers of cells of *Asterionella formosa* (in 10^9 cells per m³; depth range 0–5 m in 1952 and 1958, 0–10 m in 1959), and the chlorophyll *a* content in mg/m³ (depth range 0–10 m); (b) the penetration of light in 3 or 4 spectral regions expressed as the depth interval in which a reduction to 5 per cent occurs, with the corresponding scale of the vertical extinction coefficient (k) also indicated; (c) lake level. From J. F. Talling, Self-shading effects in natural populations of a planktonic diatom, *Wetter und Leben* (1960),*12*:239, fig. 1.

of this with a fall in concentration of either nitrate-nitrogen or phosphate to any definite level. Furthermore, the concentrations of these nutrients left in the water after the decline in the population were sufficient to support appreciable further growth. Similarly, amounts of inorganic carbon and calcium seem to have been sufficient to provide for much larger populations than were observed On the other hand, the decrease in numbers of *Asterionella* has coincided over a period of many years (Lund, 1950; Lund *et al.*, 1963) with a drop in dissolved silica concentration below 0.5 mg/liter (see Fig. 22). This agrees with an observation of Pearsall (1932) that diatoms cannot multiply

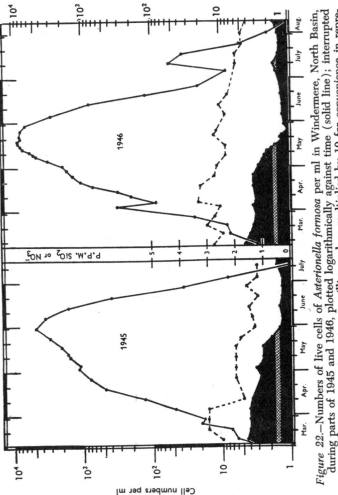

Figure 22.—Numbers of live cells of *Asterionella formosa* per ml in Windermere, North Basin, during parts of 1945 and 1946, plotted logarithmically against time (solid line); interrupted line, nitrate nitrogen in parts per million, values multiplied by 10 for convenience in representation; solid black, dissolved silica in parts per million with the 0.5 parts per million level cross-hatched. After J. W. G. Lund, Studies on *Asterionella formosa* Hass. II. Nutrient depletion and the spring maximum, *J. Ecol.* (1950), 38:6, fig. 3 (Blackwell Scientific Publications Ltd., Oxford, Eng.).

appreciably if the concentration of silica is below this level. Jørgensen (1957) found the growth of various freshwater diatom species both in culture and in lakes to be limited at silica concentrations somewhat lower than this. Observations on marine species do not seem to justify any definite conclusions, and *Skeletonema costatum* appears to be able to grow, producing a very thin siliceous wall, when the silica supply is greatly reduced (Braarud, 1962).

It is a matter of some difficulty to decide in any given instance whether a particular nutrient is limiting phytoplankton growth or not. The concentration found in the water represents the balance between consumption and supply, and a low concentration is not necessarily an indication that a nutrient is in short supply. As we have already seen (p. 26), the concentration at which a given nutrient becomes limiting varies according to the level of other factors, and there are considerable discrepancies between observations in culture and in natural waters. The rather good agreement between laboratory and field observations on silica limitation of diatoms just reported is perhaps exceptional and related to the special metabolic interrelations of this element and its low turnover rate in the water but even this agreement is dependent to a certain extent on the level of other factors. Hughes and Lund (1962) found that the addition of small amounts of phosphate to Windermere water permitted the growth of so large a crop of *Asterionella* that all the silica present was incorporated into the cells. The regular observed relationship between the spring maximum of *Asterionella* in Windermere and silica concentration thus seems to be contingent on the concentration of phosphate in the lake water and the rate of growth of the diatom as determined by the prevailing temperature and light conditions.

Gerloff and Skoog (1954; 1957) have proposed that the cell contents of elements such as nitrogen and phosphorus may be used as a measure of their availability in the water. As pointed out in Chapter IV, division of algal cells can continue if the nitrogen supply is withdrawn until a certain limiting concentration of this element in the cells is reached. Similarly, with phosphorus there may be "luxury consumption" when supply of the element is ample, resulting in a surplus in the cells which can be drawn upon to maintain growth when the supply is exhausted (Mackereth, 1953). Gerloff and Skoog studied *Microcystis aeruginosa* in particular and determined in laboratory experiments the cell concentrations of phosphorus and nitrogen below which cell division would not occur. The results given in Figure 23, for example, show that yield diminishes when cell nitrogen falls below 4 per cent on a dry weight basis. Gerloff and Skoog argued that if analysis of *M. aeruginosa* from a lake shows a value higher than this, then nitrogen cannot be limiting for growth. The method can be refined by making allowance for the variable production of mucilage by this species in the estimation of dry weight. On this basis Gerloff and Skoog concluded that nitrogen, but not phosphorus, limits growth of *M. aeruginosa* in the lakes of southern Wisconsin. This method seems a useful one, but it is desirable to know how much the limiting cell concentration of an element may change according to the level of other environmental factors. It seems probable

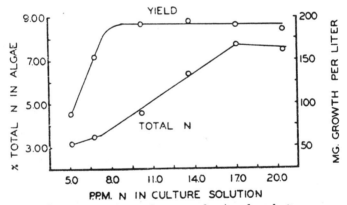

Figure 23.—Total yield (mg dry wt per liter) and total nitrogen content as a percentage of dry weight of *Microcystis aeruginosa* grown for 14 days in medium containing various levels of nitrate-nitrogen. From G. C. Gerloff, and F. Skoog, Cell contents of nitrogen and phosphorus as a measure of their availability for growth of *Microcystis aeruginosa*, Ecology (1954), 35:350, fig. 3.

that there would be some variation, at least, according to temperature and light intensity.

Another approach is to supplement samples of water with mineral nutrients, singly or in combination, and observe the effect on the phytoplankton. Ryther and Guillard (1959) have done this, using the photosynthetic uptake of C^{14} from bicarbonate as a measure of algal activity. In water samples taken in the northwestern Atlantic and in the Sargasso Sea they found that, rather than nitrogen or phosphorus, silicate and one or more components of their iron-trace metal mixture were limiting photosynthesis. Using a similar method, Goldman (1961) found that in Brooks Lake, Alaska, magnesium was the most limiting element in June when there was a peak in phytoplankton with Chrysophyta and Chlorophyta dominating. Addition of phosphate also produced some increase at this time. Later, nitrate also became limiting. In Castle Lake, California, additions of 0.1 ppm or less of molybdenum produced stimulation of photosynthesis in samples taken at various times in the year (Goldman, 1960). This method is not without its pitfalls. Addition of a nutrient element such as potassium, calcium, or magnesium may give better growth by altering the ratio of monovalent to divalent ions (Miller and Fogg, 1957), even though the element itself is not limiting. A salt may contain trace elements as impurities in sufficient amounts to make good a deficiency, and addition of phosphate may result in precipitation and complications due to consequent adsorption of ions.

CARBON DIOXIDE. Little information is available concerning the carbon dioxide requirements of phytoplankton. Perhaps the concentrations of carbon dioxide and/or bicarbonate found in most lake or sea waters are not sufficiently high to be saturating for photosynthesis under high light intensities. Paasche (unpublished) found that the rate of photosynthesis of *Coccolithus huxleyi* in sea water is carbon dioxide limited at high light intensities. On the other hand, it is not often that the concentration of carbon dioxide and/or bicarbonate in open sea waters is appreciably reduced by photosynthesis. Talling (1960*a*), for example, found no reduction due to carbon dioxide exhaustion in rate of photosynthesis of *Chaetoceros affinis* in suspensions of 19 to 46 cells per mm³ in natural sea water incubated for periods of 1-3 hours *in situ* in the sea. In dense phytoplankton blooms, however, the rate of carbon dioxide supply may become limiting, especially in fresh water. Wright (1960), for example, found evidence of carbon dioxide limitation of photosynthesis when the density of the standing crop of phytoplankton was high in Canyon Ferry Reservoir, Montana. Steemann Nielsen (1955) has recorded a particularly clear instance in a Danish lake very rich in mineral nutrients from sewage effluent. The *p*H of the water rose as high as 10.2, and it was estimated that between 60 and 100 g of carbon dioxide were absorbed per m² per month at the height of the summer season. Such limitation, however, does not result in complete cessation of growth and is unlikely to be the cause of the ending of the spring outburst.

ORGANIC GROWTH FACTORS. Many plankton algae are known to have requirements for substances such as thiamine, vitamin B_{12}, and biotin (Droop, 1962*b*; Provasoli, 1963), and it is possible that the concentrations of such substances in natural waters may sometimes be limiting. These and other organic growth factors are normally present in trace amounts in both fresh water (Hutchinson, 1957) and sea water (Provasoli, 1963). Vitamin B_{12} shows a seasonal variation in concentration in the sea, that in summer being extremely low; and it is lower in concentration in the open sea as compared with coastal waters. There is some disagreement as to whether this vitamin is ever a limiting factor. Droop has maintained that the lowest concentration found in sea water is still sufficient to provide for a dense diatom bloom, but admits that this finding is based on determinations of the effect of vitamin B_{12} concentration on final yields, and that if the effect on relative growth were determined, it might be different. Provasoli, on the other hand, has urged the view that vitamin B_{12} may be an important limiting factor in production, and both Goldman (in Riley, in the press), with freshwater phytoplankton, and McLaughlin (in Riley, in the press), with marine phytoplankton, have found that small additions of vitamin B_{12} have stimulatory effects on photosynthesis as measured by the C^{14} method. It is evident that in laboratory cultures the level at which the vitamin must be supplied to give maximum growth varies considerably according to the conditions of culture, and, furthermore, there is the uncertainty as to how much of the vitamin measured by bioassay in a natural water is available to phytoplankton species: much of it could be in bound form and unavailable to non-phagotrophic species (for references see Droop, 1962*b*; Provasoli, 1963; Riley, in the press). In view of these uncertainties the question of the importance of vitamin B_{12} in limiting phytoplankton growth must be left open for the present. It may be noted that Lund (1950; Lund *et al.*, 1963) did not take account of organic growth factors in his otherwise remarkably comprehensive studies with *Asterionella*.

AUTOINHIBITORS. As far as I am aware, there is no strong evidence of production by a phytoplankton species of an autoinhibitor in sufficient concentration to bring growth to a standstill. Considering the relatively low population densities which are usually involved, the eventuality of this happening seems remote.

LOSS IN OUTFLOW. The factors that have been considered so far are all such as may operate in laboratory cultures. In addition there are other factors, not normally operative in artificial cultures, which are important under natural conditions. Thus, there is usually a flow of water through a lake and consequently a loss of phytoplankton in the outflow. A sudden flood may therefore wash a plankton bloom out, but where the retention time is long, the loss is negligible. For *Asterionella* in Windermere, Lund (1950) concluded that, during the spring maximum, loss in the outflow is more or less compensated for by the nutrients imported in the inflow.

BUOYANCY. Buoyancy is a most important factor in phytoplankton growth and has been considered particularly by Lund (1959). Obviously, to be successful a plankton species, unless it is to be dependent on a high mixing rate in the water, must either be motile or else have a relatively slow rate of sinking, since otherwise it will not be able to maintain a position in the photic zone. There are many different features which are, or have been, reported to be concerned in flotation:

a) High surface-to-volume ratio. The greater the total surface area of the organism relative to its volume, the greater will be the friction between it and the water, and the more slowly it will sink. The striking elaboration of form encountered among phytoplankton species (see the frontispiece) gives them a high surface/volume ratio, which is perhaps of biological advantage in decreasing the rate of sinking. It will also, of course, increase the relative rate of absorption of nutrients (p. 19) and, possibly, by presenting a more awkward mouthful, discourage grazing animals. However, many species which have elaborate forms are enveloped in mucilage, as may be easily demonstrated by mounting them in negative stain, and this presumably offsets the advantages which elaboration of form confers.

b) Selective accumulation of ions. Gross and Zeuthen (1948) put forward evidence suggesting that the specific gravity of the marine diatom *Ditylum brightwelli* is maintained at a low value by preferential absorption of monovalent as against divalent ions —a solution containing only monovalent ions such as Na^+ and Cl^- having a lower specific gravity than an isotonic solution containing divalent ions as well. Bechlemikev *et al.* (quoted by Braarud, 1962) have shown by direct analysis that the cell sap of the giant diatom *Ethmodiscus rex* does actually contain reduced concentrations of divalent ions, especially magnesium, as compared with sea water. This situation would need to be maintained by active metabolism. Steele and Yentsch (1960) observed that the settling rate of actively dividing cells of *Skeletonema costatum* in culture was about one-half that of senescent cells. Since it is presumably the vacuole of the cell in which the selective accumulation of ions occurs, this mechanism would be expected to be most effective in large species with highly vacuolated cells (Braarud, 1962). Although the suggestion of Gross and Zeuthen is plausible for marine phytoplankton, it does not seem possible that it can apply in fresh water, the density of which is only of the order of 0.003 per cent greater than that of pure water. Observations on the freshwater species *Asterionella formosa* under a variety of conditions show that

Plate 3. A bloom of *Microcystis aeruginosa* in Lake Mendota, Wisconsin. Photograph by A. D. Hasler.

the cells are always heavier than water and sink if there is no turbulence (Lund, 1959).

c) Gas vacuoles. Many blue-green algae have the peculiar characteristic, found among no other organisms except certain bacteria and one or two species of protozoa, of having spaces containing gas within their protoplasts. These gas vacuoles undoubtedly lower the specific gravity of the cells sufficiently to cause them to float. If the gas vacuoles are destroyed by sudden pressure, the cells lose their buoyancy. The metabolic processes leading to the production of gas vacuoles are unknown, but, once formed, the vacuoles are stabilized by the formation of a lipoid wall and then, by diffusive exchange, come to contain a gas mixture approximating in composition that dissolved in water (for references see Fogg, 1941). Planktonic blue-green algae, such as *Microcystis,* containing these vacuoles, commonly accumulate in a dense layer at the water surface in calm weather, a phenomenon known as "water bloom" (Plate 3). Most of the water-bloom-forming blue-green algae are freshwater species, but *Trichodesmium erythraeum* is a marine plankton form which has gas vacuoles. Talling (1957a) gives an example of *Anabaena flos-aquae* collecting at the surface of a shallow reservoir off the Nile during the strong diurnal thermal stratification, then being uniformly dispersed through the water column by the nocturnal mixing (Fig. 24). Obviously, it is not of uncomplicated biological advantage to have a specific gravity less than that of water, since the cells may sometimes become so concentrated at the surface that nutrients and oxygen may become depleted.

d) Fat accumulation. It is generally supposed that many plankton species are able to float because their mean specific gravity is lowered by accumulation of fat. Undoubtedly, a form such as *Botryococcus braunii,* which contains lipoids up to 30 or 40 per cent of its dry weight, floats for this reason (Plate 1), but the evidence that fat accumulation enables diatoms to float is rather poor. Diatoms with conspicuous fat droplets in their protoplasts often have thickened silica walls, so that the cells are heavy and sink. Furthermore, laboratory experiments (p. 47) suggest that

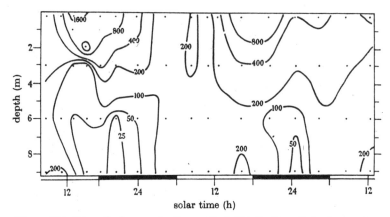

Figure 24.—Diurnal changes in the vertical distribution of *Anabaena flos-aquae* var. *intermedia* f. *spiroides* in a Nile reservoir from October 6 to 8, 1955. Isopleths (lines of equal numbers) show the density of this helically-coiled filamentous alga in coil-turns per ml. From J. F. Talling, Diurnal changes of stratification and photosynthesis in some tropical African waters, *Proc. roy. Soc., B* (1957), *147*:67, fig. 7.

fat accumulation is related to cell breakdown, and hence, that cells containing large amounts of fat are perhaps not viable.

e) Mucilage production. This is very common among phytoplankton and must have some effect in reducing the mean specific gravity of the cell.

Since movement through the water may be of great importance for the absorption of nutrients, it may actually be advantageous for a cell to sink. Munk and Riley (1952) pointed out that transfer of dissolved substances between the environment and the cell will be faster if the concentration gradient is kept steep by movement of the medium past the cell, *i.e.*, if nutrients are continually renewed in the impoverished zone adjacent to the cell. Sinking will provide such "forced convection." Munk and Riley have derived formulae for the rate of nutrient absorption by various algae approximating the shapes of spheres, discs, cylinders, and plates, and have shown that division rates in diatoms are related to their calculated sinking rates.

The success of a plankton species thus appears to depend on

a nice regulation of buoyancy, and one gets the impression that most species have a specific gravity greater than that of water but are maintained in the photic zone by turbulence. Steele and Yentsch (1960) have shown that a maximum in phytoplankton chlorophyll at the bottom of the photic zone is due to a decreased sinking rate of cells in this region. They argue that this is not accounted for by density changes in the water alone but that the cells themselves increase their buoyancy when they reach dark, nutrient-rich waters. They carried out experiments showing that this actually does occur with cultured material of *Skeletonema costatum*.

An example of a plankton alga whose growth period is curtailed through sinking is provided by *Melosira italica* sub-species *subarctica*. Lund (1954, 1955) has shown that it sinks rapidly, at 3 to 5 times the rate of *Asterionella formosa*, so that decrease in numbers in the water occurs as turbulence diminishes. The diatom disappears almost completely from the lake while it is stratified (Fig. 25). *M. italica* is consequently most abundant in the lakes of the English Lake District between autumn and late spring. The filaments on settling out pass into the deposits and remain there until resuspended. Lund has shown experimentally that a proportion of the cells can remain alive, but not growing, under anaerobic conditions in the dark for as long as three years.

GRAZING BY ANIMALS. This may have great effects on phytoplankton increase, as the following hypothetical illustration of Harvey (1945) shows. If 100 cells per liter undergo 6 successive cycles of division, the final population would be expected to be 6,400 cells per liter. If, however, 1 cell in every 10 is eaten in the intervals between divisions, the population will reach but 3,400 cells per liter, although only 413 cells have been eaten.

It is a necessary condition for the occurrence of the spring phytoplankton outbursts that, at the outset, the numbers of animals grazing on the algae should be negligible. There is a delay in zooplankton increase until the algae reach the threshold density necessary for its reproduction, and the rate of multiplication is slow as compared with that of the algae. The effect of

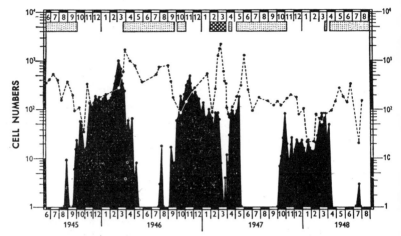

Figure 25.—The abundance of *Melosira italica* sub-species *subarctica* on the deposits and in the plankton of Blelham Tarn, 1945–48. Live cells per ml in the 0–5 water column, solid black; in unit volume of deposit at 13 m, interrupted line, both plotted on a logarithmic scale. Periods of stratification are indicated by the rectangles at the top: dotted, direct stratification; checkered, inverse stratification under ice. From J. W. G. Lund, The seasonal cycle of the plankton diatom, *Melosira italica* (Ehr.) Kütz. subsp. subarctica D. Müll., *J. Ecol.* (1954), *42*:156, fig. 2 (Blackwell Scientific Publications Ltd., Oxford, Eng.).

grazing is therefore likely to be appreciable only in the later stages of spring growth. In cold waters, in which the development of herbivores is extremely slow, the maximum of phytoplankton is evidently not controlled by grazing (Cushing, 1959*a*). In temperate waters the herbivores develop more quickly, and their numbers become sufficient toward the end of the spring growth period for them to have an appreciable effect on the course of phytoplankton increase. Cushing (1959*b*) and Steele (1963), on the basis of mathematical analysis of the course of phytoplankton increase in relation to probable controlling factors, consider that grazing is the most important factor bringing about the cessation of spring growth in waters around Britain, but as Riley (1963) points out, this may not be true in other regions. In fresh water, grazing is, perhaps, of less importance. Lund (1959) is of the opinion that it has no appreciable effect on the spring increase of *Asterionella formosa*. In the English lakes the main development of zooplankton follows that of the phytoplankton. There is no evidence that the animals eat *Asterionella*, and it seems that their principal foods are bacteria and protozoa, which develop at the expense of the dying phytoplankton. Nauwerck (1963) has similarly concluded for Lake Erken in Sweden that phytoplankton is of secondary importance as a direct source of food for zooplankton. It is to be expected, of course, that nannoplankton are grazed to a greater extent than comparatively large forms such as *Asterionella*, but the difficulty of recognizing their remains makes direct evidence of this hard to obtain.

PARASITIZATION. This has been suggested as a factor controlling the growth of marine phytoplankton, but there appears to be little definite evidence to support this view (ZoBell, 1946). Many freshwater algae, however, are known to be parasitized by fungi. *Asterionella formosa* is attacked by the chytridaceous fungus *Rhizophidium planktonicum*. This parasite is nearly always present when the host is, but for most of the year its frequency is too low to reduce appreciably the numbers of *Asterionella* in the English lakes, and it seems that, although it may affect the course of the spring increase, it is rarely the cause of its end. The course of an epidemic is shown in Figure 26; such occurrences are most frequent in autumn and winter (Canter and Lund, 1948). So far it has not proved possible to grow *Rhizophidium* in artificial culture or to correlate the onset of epidemics with any single factor or group of factors.

There is nothing corresponding to the stationary phase, as usually observed in laboratory cultures, following the cessation of the spring growth of phytoplankton. This is attributable to the effects of grazing and sedimentation in rapidly depleting a population which is not actively multiplying and to the killing, by high light intensities, of cells suffering from deficiency of certain nutrients. This evidently happens with *Asterionella formosa*, cells of which can continue to grow in the absence of sufficient supplies of silica, a process which results in self-destruction. The dead cells become covered with a mass of bacteria and sink

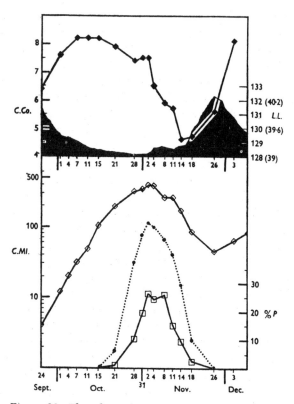

Figure 26.—The relationship between numbers of a parasite, *Rhizophidium planktonicum*, and its host, *Asterionella formosa*, in Esthwaite Water, autumn 1946.
C.Co., average number of live cells per *Asterionella*
colony (a solid line with black diamonds); *C.Ml.*, number of live *Asterionella* cells per ml (a solid line with
white diamonds) and the number of live *Rhizophidium*
cells per ml (a dotted line with black circles), both
plotted on a logarithmic scale; *L.L.*, Windermere,
North Basin lake level in feet (meters in parentheses)
shown solid black; *%P*, percentage of *Asterionella* cells
infected by living *Rhizophidium* cells (a solid line with
white squares). From H. M. Canter and J. W. G. Lund,
Studies on plankton parasites. I. Fluctuations in the
numbers of *Asterionella formosa* Hass. in relation to
fungal epidemics, *New Phytol.* (1948), 47:243, fig. 1
(Blackwell Scientific Publications Ltd., Oxford, Eng.).

rapidly, forming a flocculent deposit on the lake bottom (Lund, *et al.*, 1963).

The most thorough studies of growth of phytoplankton in the spring are undoubtedly those of Lund, and as this chapter is concluded, it is worth repeating a point that he has constantly emphasized, namely, that his conclusions hold good only for *Asterionella formosa* in the English Lake District, and that for other species and for the same species in other parts of the world, the factors controlling growth may be quite different.

VII

SOME OTHER ASPECTS
OF PHYTOPLANKTON PERIODICITY

During the summer period, following the spring maximum, there is normally a period of two months or so in temperate lakes and seas when the standing crop of phytoplankton remains at a relatively low and steady level. The low level of the standing crop is attributable to the depletion of nutrients from the photic zone by the sedimentation of the greater part of the cells produced in the spring maximum, thermal stratification stabilizing the water column so that there is no replenishment by mixing from below. The comparative stability in the amount of phytoplankton is attributable to the achievement of approximate equilibrium between it and the herbivore population, the algal reproductive rate being more or less balanced by the loss through grazing (Cushing, 1959a). A similar situation is characteristic of tropical lakes and seas throughout the year. These conditions are quite unlike those in a culture of limited volume and more resemble those in a chemostat culture (Riley, in the press). Although nutrient concentrations in the water are low, there is continual regeneration by means of the zooplankton and bacteria, so that, as in the chemostat, growth is limited by the rate of supply of a nutrient in limiting amount. The rate of turnover of a nutrient element may be surprisingly high. Watt and Hayes (1963) have estimated the turnover times in inshore waters off Halifax, Nova Scotia, as 1.5 days for dissolved inorganic phosphorus, 2.0 days for particulate phosphorus, and 0.5 days for dissolved organic phosphorus.

Such an equilibrium may be disturbed by changes in hydrographical conditions. Circulation and mixing may occur in tropical waters, but generally somewhat irregularly. Because of the greater change in density per degree at higher temperatures, a given amount of cooling produces much more active convection currents in a tropical water than in a temperate water. Continued cooling may thus lead to turnover, without the necessity of wind action, and a consequent enrichment with nutrients from below. Lake Victoria, which has moderately high densities of phytoplankton and a high rate of production throughout the year (Talling, 1961*b*), seems to owe its fertility to the efficient mixing brought about by seiche action in its extensive but shallow basin. A semi-tropical part of the Sargasso Sea, so far the only region of open sea in which the seasonal cycle and annual variability of primary productivity have been studied, has special hydrographical features (Ryther, 1963). The most important of these is a permanent thermocline at 400–500 m, above which a summer thermocline develops at about 100 m. Phytoplankton production remains at a low and fairly constant level throughout the year except when winter temperatures fall low enough for the upper thermocline to break down so that mixing of the water occurs down to the lower thermocline. The amount of nutrients thus made available is small but sufficient to produce an increase in phytoplankton, which gradually builds up to a maximum in the spring (see p. 97). In mild winters thermal stratification persists in the upper layers of water, and the production is correspondingly less.

From time to time there occur in the sea dense accumulations of phytoplankton known as "red tides," which not only are striking in themselves but also attract further attention by leading to mass mortality of marine invertebrates and fish. Most commonly, the organisms concerned are Dinophyceae, colored red by accumulation of carotenoids, but the term "red tide" has been extended to include phytoplankton blooms of other colors and composed of species belonging to other groups. Since red tides appear to be characteristic of tropical waters and temperate waters in the summer, the phenomenon calls for some comment here. A typical example has been described by Paredes (1962) from the coast of Angola, where it is of fairly regular occurrence. From the air it was seen as vast parallel areas of reddish water. It persisted from 15 to 20 days and resulted in the death of large numbers of fish and crabs. The principal organism concerned was *Exuviella baltica* associated with other dinoflagellates and with diatoms. Red tides are usually confined to coastal waters, and undoubtedly one necessary condition is a high concentration of nutrients, as produced, for example, by upwelling or outflow of fresh water. There must also be paucity of zooplankton using the particular species for food and, possibly, particular conditions of light and temperature. The high population densities seem to be produced not directly by growth but by concentration at the surface as a result of wind and current action (Ryther, 1955). The death of fish and other animals may sometimes be produced by mechanical clogging of their gills or by deoxygenation and production of substances such as hydrogen sulfide following decomposition of the phytoplankton, but certain red tide organisms, e.g., *Gymnodinium veneficum*, are known to produce specific toxins (Abbott and Ballantine, 1957).

The second maximum of phytoplankton which sometimes occurs in temperate waters in the autumn is perhaps principally due to augmentation of the nutrient supply brought about by increased circulation and mixing. Possibly a decline in the herbivore population may be a contributory factor (Cushing, 1959a). Although the nutrient supply is not limiting, phytoplankton growth is restricted by the diminishing light and the increased turbulence removing cells from the photic zone. These conditions may be considered as approximating those in the turbidostat type of continuous culture (Riley, in the press). If the mixing rate is very great, the population in the photic zone will be depleted faster than it grows, and no autumn maximum will occur. This was evidently the situation in the autumn of 1947 in Windermere (Fig. 18).

While it is thus possible to suggest explanations in qualitative terms for the major features of phytoplankton periodicity, our knowledge will approach completeness only when a full quantitative account of the effects of various conditions can be given and used to predict the future course of plankton increase and decrease. It is not within the scope of this book to discuss in detail the mathematical models of plankton periodicity which have been put forward thus far, but perhaps an indication of the assumptions on which they are based and of their adequacy may be useful here. Riley (1963) has used the following general equation as the basis for his analysis:

$$\frac{dP}{dt} = P \ (P_h - R - G),$$

where P is the total phytoplankton population per unit of sea surface, P_h is a photosynthetic coefficient, R is a coefficient of phytoplankton respiration, and G is a grazing coefficient. P_h was estimated by an empirical equation from measurements of incident radiation, transparency of the water, depth of the mixed layer, and concentration of phosphate, which was taken as a measure of the general level of nutrients. Phytoplankton respiration was assessed from experimental data and assumed to increase exponentially with rise in temperature. The grazing coefficient was taken as proportional to the observed herbivore population. Several sets of data have been examined in this way by approximate integration over successive short periods of time during which the environmental conditions were assumed to remain constant. This gave curves showing the seasonal changes in relative terms. Three of these calculated curves, assigned arbitrary absolute values to give the best fit statistically with the observed phytoplankton populations, are shown together with the actual observed seasonal cycles in Figure 27. In spite of the many simplifying assumptions—the phytoplankton population, for example, is assumed to be homogeneous and the zooplankton to be non-selective in its grazing—the agreement

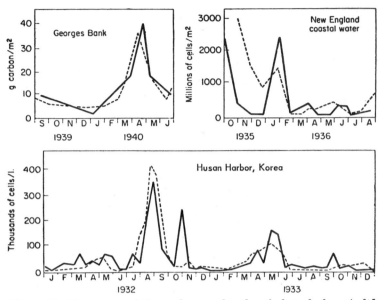

Figure 27.—Comparison of observed seasonal cycles of phytoplankton (solid lines) with cycles calculated from a mathematical model. After G. A. Riley, Theory of food-chain relations in the ocean, in *The Sea*, ed. M. N. Hill, vol. 2 (1963), 442, fig. 1.

between the calculated and observed curves is reasonably good. It must be remembered, however, that the situations chosen for this analysis were presumably selected for their comparative simplicity. Furthermore, besides the basic physical parameters—incident radiation, temperature, and vertical eddy diffusivity—on which phytoplankton growth ultimately depends, others, such as transparency of the water, phosphate concentration, and herbivore numbers, which are dependent on the phytoplankton population itself, were used. More fundamental approaches, such as those made by Riley and his collaborators (Riley, 1963) by Steele (1958), and by Cushing (1959*b*), inevitably give less satisfactory agreement between theoretical and observed values. However, the great value of these attempts is that they show where knowledge is inadequate and suggest methods and hypotheses for further investigation.

It has been assumed in most quantitative studies that the properties and responses of phytoplankton are unvarying. As we saw in Chapter IV, this is far from being so in cultures, and, although conditions in natural waters are not usually so extreme as they may be in the laboratory, we should expect something of the great variability in intensity and pattern of metabolism of which algae are capable to be exhibited in natural populations. Visual evidence that this happens is provided by those plankton species which accumulate large quantities of carotenoids. *Botryococcus braunii*, for example, may be encountered in both the green and orange forms in lakes and presumably has the corresponding high and low rates of photosynthesis and growth observed in cultures.

Quantitative evidence that variation in rate of metabolism occurs in natural populations is provided by the estimates of the ratio of photosynthesis at light saturation to chlorophyll (mg C per hr/mg chlorophyll) which are available in the literature and which have been summarized by Ryther and Yentsch (1957). Not only is the standard deviation of the ratio in any one situation high, but mean values from different situations show more than a twofold variation, *i.e.*, from 2.1 to 5.7. There are, of course, the difficulties that in an estimation of chlorophyll in natural waters a distinction cannot be made between that in living algae and in detritus, and that chlorophyll is not the only pigment concerned in photosynthesis. On the face of it, however, these results suggest variation in metabolic activity of natural phytoplankton at least as great as that described for laboratory cultures in Chapter IV. Rodhe *et al.* (1958) found in Lake Erken that the ratio of carbon fixed in the 1–2 m layer to the corresponding amounts of chlorophyll remained at a rather constant low value during the spring growth but rose in the summer months to higher values, which showed no simple pattern of variation. Similarly Steele and Baird (1961) found that in two different areas of the North Sea, in the waters of which there did not appear to be any appreciable amount of "dead" chlorophyll, there were distinct seasonal trends in the photosynthesis/chlorophyll ratio from about 1 in spring to about

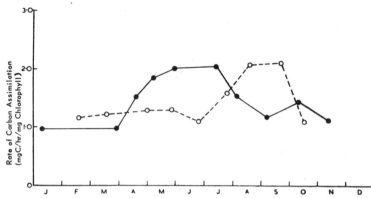

Figure 28.—The monthly average ratios of carbon assimilation per hour at 10,000 lux to chlorophyll concentration for two areas of the North Sea; Fladen, 0–30 m, solid line; Aberdeen Bay, dashed line. From J. H. Steele, and I. E. Baird, Relations between primary production, chlorophyll and particulate carbon, *Limnol. oceanogr.* (1961), 6:77, fig. 8.

2 in summer, with a decline again in autumn (Fig. 28). The trend in the ratio corresponds to that found in cultures as they become nitrogen deficient. Fogg (1959), for example, reported results for *Monodus subterraneus*, which give a ratio of 1.6 for actively growing cells and 6.1 for nitrogen-deficient ones. Steele and Baird comment that light adaptation is not a sufficient explanation of the change, and that since the changes on the Fladen ground are roughly opposite to the changes in nutrient concentration, "the variations in photosynthetic efficiency cannot be explained in terms of nutrient limitation." This latter suggestion seems quite mistaken. At least for nitrogen, the photosynthesis/chlorophyll ratio *rises* with increasing deficiency, as Spoehr and Milner pointed out as long ago as 1949. The seasonal changes observed by Rodhe *et al.* and by Steele and Baird seem to be just those expected in populations becoming progressively more nutrient deficient into the summer, then receiving a further supply in late summer. Evidence of similar trends in metabolism is also provided by the carbon/chlorophyll ratio. Steele (1962) observed a rise of about tenfold in this ratio in the open North Sea from spring to summer. This

corresponded well with the observed depletion of nutrients and was of the same order of magnitude as that found by Steele and Baird (1962) in cultures.

Determinations of the elementary composition or the contents of major fractions such as carbohydrate, fat, and protein in phytoplankton populations might also be expected to give some indication of their metabolic characteristics. However, few such analyses have been made on natural material, and some of these are of questionable validity, so that the available data (summarized by Strickland, 1960) are of little use for the present purposes.

Finally, in this chapter, the possibility of short-term variations in growth and metabolism should be considered. It might be expected that the regular alternation of light and dark in the natural habitat would induce a considerable degree of synchronization of cell division and consequently a diurnal periodicity in metabolic activity. It is well established that pronounced diurnal rhythms of photosynthetic activity are shown by phytoplankton. Doty and Oguri (1957) measured radiocarbon uptake by samples of natural marine plankton from surface waters in the tropics for short periods under constant conditions. They found that the same population photosynthesized nearly 6 times as fast under such conditions at 8 A.M. as it did at 7 P.M. Similar behavior was found in samples from deep water. This diurnal fluctuation was found to decrease going north from the equator and ceased altogether at a latitude of 60° to 70° N. In accordance with these observations, Shimada (1958) found three- to fourfold diurnal variation at 18° N, and Yentsch and Ryther (1957) a twofold variation at Wood's Hole, 42° N. In fresh waters in Germany, Ohle (1958, 1961) has observed decreases of about 20 per cent in photosynthetic activity between morning and afternoon.

The explanation of these variations is not obvious. Their magnitude indicates changes in rate of photosynthesis rather than of respiration, and they are accompanied by corresponding changes in chlorophyll (Yentsch and Ryther, 1957), so that the photosynthesis/chlorophyll ratio remains approximately constant

(Ohle, 1961). Steemann Nielsen and Jørgensen (1962) considered the effect to be due to a reduced rate of chlorophyll synthesis at high light intensities combined with grazing by zooplankton; actual destruction of chlorophyll, it was pointed out, occurs only after photosynthesis has ceased altogether. Ohle (1961), who found no evidence of endogenous rhythms in the phytoplankton populations which he studied, showed that the variation is reduced if the turbulence in the water is increased. He postulated that the decreased rates of photosynthesis were brought about by accumulation of waste products within the cells. On the other hand, the occurrence of endogenous rhythms in cell division in some dinoflagellates under natural conditions is well established (Sweeney and Hastings, 1962), so that one might reasonably expect to find diurnal rhythms contributing to the observed variations in photosynthesis. If synchronization of cell division were to occur in lakes or the sea, we would expect to find Tamiya's D-type cells predominating in the morning and L cells predominating later on in the day. This would agree with the observed variations in photosynthesis and chlorophyll. These various explanations are not necessarily mutually exclusive, and it might well be that the observed fluctuations are due to a combination of effects. The decrease in variation at high latitudes may be related to the lower light intensities prevailing there.

VIII

PHYTOPLANKTON DISTRIBUTION AND SEASONAL SUCCESSION

I t is a useful simplification in many kinds of investigation to regard phytoplankton as a single homogeneous entity, and it must be largely true that the total biomass of phytoplankton is determined by the physical and chemical factors in the environment and is not dependent on the species which are represented in it. Nevertheless, phytoplankton normally consists of a heterogeneous collection of organisms, and the problems posed by the distribution and seasonal succession of the species present are not only of interest in themselves, but, since qualitative differences may have effects on the higher components of the food chain, are of economic importance.

The spatial distribution of phytoplankton species may be limited by barriers such as land or water masses of unfavorable temperature or salinity, but otherwise the operative factors are the same as those determining distribution in time or, in other words, succession. For present purposes it is more appropriate to concentrate on the problems of seasonal succession. For special consideration of spatial distribution the reader is referred to Braarud (1962) and Riley (in the press). An article by Johnson and Brinton (1963) may also be found useful although concerned primarily with zooplankton.

The general character of phytoplankton succession during the course of the year may be illustrated by results reported by Rodhe *et al.* (1958) for Erken, a eutrophic lake in central Sweden (Fig. 29). In both the years covered by these observations diatoms made up the larger part of the standing crop in April and May, being followed by flagellates, such as *Rhodomonas minuta* and *Dinobryon divergens,* and these by green and blue-green algae. Although there was a general similarity be-

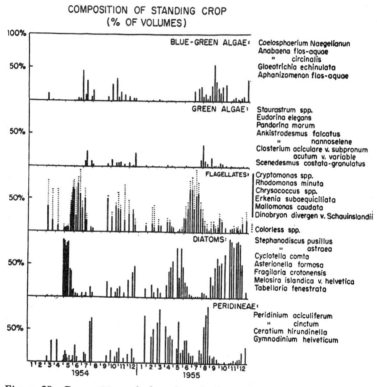

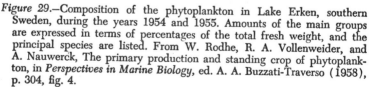

Figure 29.—Composition of the phytoplankton in Lake Erken, southern Sweden, during the years 1954 and 1955. Amounts of the main groups are expressed in terms of percentages of the total fresh weight, and the principal species are listed. From W. Rodhe, R. A. Vollenweider, and A. Nauwerck, The primary production and standing crop of phytoplankton, in *Perspectives in Marine Biology*, ed. A. A. Buzzati-Traverso (1958), p. 304, fig. 4.

tween the sequences in the two years, there was not exact repetition; the autumn diatom maximum in 1955, for example, was much more pronounced than that in 1954. It will be obvious that the factors concerned in such a succession must be various and that the interactions between them are likely to be complex. The following seem to be important:

TEMPERATURE AND LIGHT. Different species undoubtedly have different temperature and light requirements, and it could be that a particular species predominates at a particular season because the prevailing temperature and light conditions favor it. It is customary to designate plankton organisms as oligothermal, polythermal, or eurythermal, according to whether they appear to be cold-requiring, warmth-requiring, or able to tolerate a wide temperature range (Ruttner, 1953). However, the temperature at which an organism is most abundant in nature does not necessarily correspond to its optimum temperature as determined in the laboratory; the planktonic strain of *Chlorella pyrenoidosa* studied by Fogg and Belcher (1961) was isolated from Torneträsk in Swedish Lappland, in which the temperature does not rise above 7° C, yet its optimum in culture was found to be about 20° C. The discrepancies and contradictions regarding the temperature requirements of *Skeletonema costatum* are even more disturbing (Braarud, 1962); the optimum temperature for growth in the sea is variously reported as 12° to 13° C and 14° to 20° C and that for growth in culture as 20° or 30° C according to the nutrient concentrations in the medium. It may be that different strains of this species were investigated by the different workers, but it is clear that the optimum temperature varies according to the level of other factors, and adaptation very probably also plays a part. The occurrence of blue-green algae in certain situations may be directly attributable to their tolerance of high temperatures, but otherwise it seems that the abundance of a particular species can rarely be put down purely and simply to the temperature's being optimal for it. The absence of a species may, of course, be ascribable to the direct effect of unduly high or low temperatures. Similarly with the intensity, quality, and daily duration

of light there are so many possibilities of adaptation and interaction with other factors that it seems unlikely that any of these
per se can be the major factor determining the occurrence of
a species at a particular time or place.

HYDROGRAPHICAL CONDITIONS. Hydrographical conditions undoubtedly may play an important part in determining the
abundance of particular species at particular seasons. The effects
of turbulence and the differences in buoyancy among species
have already been discussed in Chapter VI, and it will be sufficient here to recall that the abundance of *Melosira italica*, in
certain lakes at least, is largely determined by the degree of
turbulence.

CONCENTRATION OF NUTRIENTS. The differing requirements of
different species for nutrients may operate to give succession.
An obvious example here is that when a diatom maximum has
come to an end because of exhaustion of silica, enough other
nutrients may yet be available to support further growth of
algae, such as Chlorophyceae, which do not require silica. Other
features of succession might be the result of changes in concentration in other nutrients and shifts in ion ratios occurring
in the water as the season advances. It seems a sad but inescap-
able conclusion that much of the painstaking investigation of
the effects of these factors on growth of phytoplankton in culture is of little use in interpreting the events in lakes or the sea.
Some workers have used final yield as their measure of the effect
of nutrient concentration on growth, whereas effects on lag
phase and the relative growth constant are undoubtedly of more
importance in determining succession. Apart from this, it has
not been sufficiently realized how much the level of other factors—light intensity, temperature, presence of organic chelating
agents, etc.—may determine the effect of a given concentration
of a nutrient.

Observation of succession in relation to the changes in the
chemistry of natural waters which actually take place seems to
offer a better approach. A notable investigation along these
lines was that of Pearsall (1932), who carried out a study of
the composition of the phytoplankton in relation to dissolved

substances in the English lakes. Some of his conclusions were as follows: (1) diatoms increase when the water is richest in phosphate, nitrate, and silica; (2) *Dinobryon divergens*, in hardwater lakes, develops maxima when the silica content falls below 5 ppm and, in all lakes, is favored by a rise in the ratio of nitrate to phosphate; (3) desmids and other green algae occur mainly during the summer depletion of nutrients, the former being favored by a low calcium content and a low nitrate/phosphate ratio; (4) the abundance of blue-green algae is correlated with high concentrations of dissolved organic matter in the water, these algae being able to increase at very low concentrations of inorganic nutrients.

As we saw in Chapter VI, Pearsall's conclusions regarding diatom growth have been substantiated by subsequent work. His inferences regarding *Dinobryon* (2, above), however, were found by Hutchinson (1944) not to hold for lakes in other regions. The appearance of this alga in Linsley Pond, Connecticut, is correlated with a rise in the nitrate/phosphate ratio but is independent of variations in dissolved silica, although in other lakes it may be correlated with falling silica concentration but not with the nitrate/phosphate ratio. Rodhe (1948) considered that *Dinobryon* is favored by reduction in phosphate concentration, but it has been grown in culture in phosphate-rich media (Talling, 1962). Pearsall's conclusion (3, above) that low calcium concentrations favor green algae, and in particular desmids, seems generally valid. However, Chu (1942) in culture experiments found that whereas *Pediastrum boryanum* favors low concentrations of calcium, the concentration of this element in nearly all fresh waters is within the optimum range for *Staurastrum paradoxum*. Chu (1943) also found that no increase or decrease of the nitrate/phosphate ratio markedly affected the growth of any of the plankton algae which he studied, so long as the concentration of these radicals remained within the optimum range for the organisms in question.

The correlation of abundance of blue-green algae with the content of dissolved organic matter found by Pearsall (4, above) seems to hold generally, but the basis for this is still obscure.

Most planktonic blue-green algae which have been grown in culture have been found to do well in mineral media devoid of organic supplements other than citrate to maintain iron in an available form (Gerloff *et al.*, 1950; Staub, 1961). Some blue-green algae are capable of growing in the dark on organic substrates, but many are obligate phototrophs (Fogg, 1956*b*). Rodhe (1948) found that *Gloeotrichia echinulata* requires an unidentified thermolabile organic growth factor, but so far only *Phormidium persicinum*, out of the 24 species examined from this point of view, has been definitely reported as having requirements for vitamin B_{12} (Droop, 1962*b*; Provasoli, 1963). Although Pearsall's correlation of abundance of blue-green algae with the dissolved organic content of the water a month earlier suggests the latter as the causative factor, it is a well-established characteristic of these algae in culture to liberate substantial quantities of extracellular organic substances (Fogg, 1952), and it might well be that the high concentrations of dissolved organic matter accompanying their mass development in lakes are produced partly by themselves. The extracellular products of blue-green algae are known to form complexes with inorganic ions (Fogg and Westlake, 1955), and it seems probable that the importance of organic substances for these algae is not so much to act as direct nutrients as to regulate the ionic environment.

Pearsall's second point about blue-green algae—that they are able to develop at very low concentrations of inorganic nutrients —has been confirmed by Hutchinson (1944). In part, this may be explained by the ability of some species to fix free nitrogen, N_2. Three species of planktonic blue-green algae which have been isolated in pure culture, viz., *Microcystis (Diplocystis) aeruginosa*, *Aphanizomenon flos-aquae* (Williams and Burris, 1952), and *Oscillatoria rubescens* (Staub, 1961), have proved not to possess the nitrogen-fixing property. No planktonic *Anabaena*, a genus which contains many nitrogen-fixing species, appears to have been studied critically in culture. Nevertheless, the indirect evidence that planktonic species of *Anabaena* fix nitrogen is convincing. Prowse and Talling (1958) found the amounts of nitrogen contained in blooms of *Anabaena flos-aquae* in the White Nile to be far in excess of that available as nitrate in the water, and Kusnezow (1959) has reported evidence showing that an *Anabaena* is the main agent of biological nitrogen fixation in Lake Tschornoje. Dugdale and Dugdale (1962), using N^{15} as a tracer, have shown vigorous fixation associated with growth of *Anabaena* spp. in Sanctuary Lake, Pennsylvania. Since this fixation was found to be light dependent, it seems probable that it was due to the *Anabaena* itself rather than to associated bacteria. Figure 30 shows the development of a maximum of *Anabaena* with a parallel increase in nitrogen fixation at a time when concentrations of ammonia and nitrate in the water were low. A rise in concentration of these two forms of combined nitrogen later suppressed nitrogen fixation but not the growth of the blue-green algae. Several non-planktonic marine species of blue-green algae have been isolated in pure culture and have been shown to be nitrogen-fixing (Stewart, 1962; Allen, 1963). There is no clear evidence that marine planktonic forms can fix nitrogen, although there are indications that *Trichodesmium,* which sometimes forms dense blooms in tropical waters, possesses the property (Dugdale, *et al.,* 1961). In summary it may be said that an ability to fix nitrogen may sometimes be the reason for the predominance of blue-green algae at times when shortage of nitrogen limits other plankton algae, but it cannot be a general explanation of their position in the seasonal succession.

Probably the relationship of succession to nutrient concentrations is the same for marine as for freshwater plankton, although less information is available. However, an apparently clear-cut instance of the dependence of a diatom maximum on the concentration of vitamin B_{12} in the waters of the Sargasso Sea has been reported by Menzel and Spaeth (1962). Using the diatom *Cyclotella nana* to assay for vitamin B_{12}, the authors found the concentration in the surface 50 m to vary from 0.03 $m\mu g$/liter down to an undetectable amount from May to October. *Coccolithus huxleyi,* which does not require vitamin B_{12}, is dominant in the phytoplankton under these conditions. The bloom of diatoms, with *Rhizosolenia stolterfothii* and *Bacteriastrum deli-*

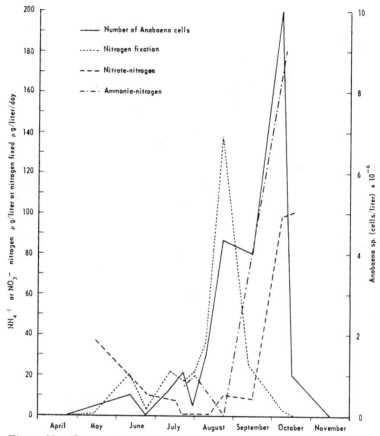

Figure 30.—Changes in concentrations of ammonia- and nitrate-nitrogen, nitrogen fixation, and numbers of *Anabaena* in the surface water of Sanctuary Lake, Pennsylvania, during 1959. Replotted data from V. A. Dugdale and R. C. Dugdale, Nitrogen metabolism in lakes. II. Role of nitrogen fixation in Sanctuary Lake, Pennsylvania, *Limnol. oceanogr.* (1962), 7:170.

catulum predominating, occurred in April when the level of B_{12} was increased to 0.06 to 0.1 mμg/liter, evidently by mixing in of deeper water. This brings us to the possibility, envisaged by Hutchinson (1944) and others, that traces of organic growth-promoting or growth-inhibiting substances produced by the algae themselves may play an important part in succession.

GROWTH-PROMOTING AND GROWTH-INHIBITING SUBSTANCES. Some evidence for the presence of growth-promoting and growth-inhibiting substances in natural waters and their rôle in determining the total biomass of phytoplankton has already been discussed (p. 72). Clearly they may be produced by specific organisms and may have specific effects on particular species, so that their rôle in interspecific competition and determining the qualitative composition of the phytoplankton may be considerable. These biologically active substances may be liberated during healthy growth or after the death of the cells, perhaps only during decomposition under particular conditions.

There is mounting evidence for the production of growth-promoting substances by algae in culture. Lewin (1958) detected thiamine in filtrates from cultures of *Coccomyxa* sp. Plant hormones of the auxin type have been demonstrated in extracts of *Chlorella* and various plankton algae, in filtrates from cultures of *Anabaena cylindrica,* and from lake water containing a nearly unialgal growth of *Oscillatoria* sp. (Bentley, 1958, 1960). Lefèvre and Jakob (1949) have found evidence for substances responsible for the growth-promoting effects of one algal species on another but have not chemically characterized such substances.

Many workers have reported that certain species inhibit the growth of others in mixed culture. Perhaps some of these effects are due to specific antibiotic substances, but since the conditions of culture have not always been strictly controlled nor the substances isolated and chemically characterized, there is considerable uncertainty. Proctor (1957), however, showed clearly that inhibition of *Haematococcus pluvialis* by *Chlamydomonas reinhardtii* is due to a fatty acid liberated on the death of the *Chlamydomonas* cells. Jakob (1961) found that *Nostoc muscorum* produces in bacteria-free culture a "dihydroxy-anthraquinone," which inhibits growth of other algae such as *Cosmarium, Phormidium,* and *Euglena.* On the other hand, in a careful study of the growth of two planktonic diatoms, *Asterionella formosa* and *Fragilaria crotonensis,* in mixed culture and in media containing culture filtrates, Talling (1957*b*) found no evidence for the production by either species of any extracellular substance which appreciably modified the growth of the other. There is a great deal of evidence that some algae produce antibacterial substances (see Fogg, 1962; Jørgensen, 1962). While these may have no direct effect on other algae, they may obviously indirectly affect competition among algal species by their effects on associated bacteria.

Zavarzina (1959) has reported the presence of a factor inhibitory to the growth of *Scenedesmus quadricauda* in various reservoir and lake waters. This factor, which could be adsorbed on activated charcoal, appeared to originate from other algae rather than from the lake mud. Smayda (1963), however, has put forward reasons for thinking that antibiosis plays no very important part in phytoplankton succession, and in view of the ready adaptation of some algae to antibiotics (see p. 26) this seems probable. Johnston (1963b) likewise concluded from his experimental studies that the quality of sea waters was primarily a matter of their content of growth-promoting substances rather than of inhibitors. These growth-promoting substances appeared to have different effects on different species, since bioassays of various seawater samples, enriched with phosphate and nitrate and containing adequate amounts of vitamin B_{12}, gave different results according to whether the assay organism was *Skeletonema costatum* or *Peridinium trochoideum*.

It is attractive to explain succession in terms of traces of biologically active substances, but clearly it is still not possible to say whether or not this is an important factor.

SELECTIVE GRAZING. If herbivores graze selectively, they may have important effects on succession. Obviously there must be some discrimination according to size, but cells may also be selected or rejected on a more subtle basis. Among the best evidence for selective grazing is that obtained by Edmondson (unpublished) from a study of the relation of egg production by rotifers in the English lakes to numbers of various phytoplankton algae and bacteria. Data from a total of 400 samples obtained over a period of two years were subjected to statistical analysis. The partial correlation coefficients obtained between egg production and numbers of a phytoplankton species presumably are a measure of the extent to which the alga was eaten, although, of course, there may be effects due to differential digestion and the chemical composition of the food organisms. The results given in Table 6 for *Keratella cochlearis* indicate that this rotifer seeks out and eats *Chrysochromulina*. *Rhodomonas,* an alga about the same size as *Chrysochromulina,* was eaten to a much smaller extent, although it was nearly twice as abundant. Other organisms, e.g., *Stichococcus* and miscellaneous flagellates, were also selected, but *Chlorella* was perhaps avoided.

TABLE 6

Relation of reproductive rate of *Keratella cochlearis* to temperature and abundance of specific food organisms in four lakes. Temperature in ° C, abundance of food organisms in µg dry wt/liter (unpublished data of Edmondson)

Independent variable	Mean value of independent variable	Partial correlation coefficient
Temperature	11.11	0.416
Chlorella	6.33	−0.007
Stichococcus	1.63	0.129
Coccomyxa	5.09	0.023
Chlamydomonas	2.32	0.013
Chrysochromulina	26.52	0.415
Miscellaneous flagellates	13.84	0.152
Colorless flagellates	18.97	0.052
Rhodomonas	49.48	0.135
Chrysococcus	7.52	0.009

Similar results were obtained for *Kellicottia longispina,* whereas a third rotifer, *Polyarthra vulgaris,* showed a high correlation with *Cryptomonas* but little correlation with anything else except temperature. These findings are in general agreement with the conclusions which Nauwerck (1963) drew from his study of the relations between zooplankton and phytoplankton in Lake Erken. Nauwerck found that, although Peridineae, diatoms, and blue-green algae were most abundant in the phytoplankton, small chrysomonads were most important, both qualitatively and quantitatively, as food for the animals. Cryptomonads came next and small green algae and small diatoms were considerably less important.

It therefore seems likely that selective grazing is common, but it remains to be seen how important it is in determining succession.

There is thus no evidence that any one factor is of over-riding importance in determining the abundance of particular species at particular seasons, and it seems probable that in each instance a complex of interacting factors is concerned. An interesting approach to dealing with this situation has been made by Margalef (1958), based mainly on his studies of phytoplankton in the Gulf of Vigo. Three stages in succession may be distinguished:

1. A phase of growth, characterized by algae, *e.g.*, small diatoms, which have small cells (and consequently a high surface/volume ratio), a preference for high concentrations of nutrients, and a relatively high rate of growth (one or two divisions per day). These algae are easily grown in crude culture.

2. A mixed community of forms, which often have bigger cells and lower relative growth rate and which are not so easily grown in culture, *e.g.*, larger diatoms.

3. A mixture of forms, many of them motile, characterized by being extremely difficult to culture and therefore presumably having complex nutritional requirements, *e.g.*, dinoflagellates, particularly red-tide organisms. Irregularities in horizontal distribution become most pronounced at this stage, with patches "changing from moment to moment like clouds in the sky."

This is perhaps a picture of general validity for temperate waters. For example, in the English lakes stage 1 would seem to be represented by *Asterionella, Melosira,* and *Chlorella,* stage 2 by *Tabellaria, Staurastrum,* and *Mallomonas,* and stage 3 by dinoflagellates and blue-green algae. Johnston (1963*a*) has commented that the phytoplankton succession in waters off the northeast coast of Scotland resembles in principle that described by Margalef and has made the interesting observation that species characteristic of stage 1, *e.g., Skeletonema* and

Thalassiosira, are sensitive to antimetabolites such as sulfanila-mide and benzimidazole, whereas later forms, *e.g., Chaetoceros* spp. and *Rhizosolenia alata,* are more resistant.

Margalef determined the index of diversity,

$$d = \frac{S-1}{\log_e N},$$

where S is the number of species and N the number of indi-viduals, at different intervals during the growing season. The index d was found to vary in a rather regular manner during the succession (Fig. 31), being between 1 and 2 at the beginning and increasing up to 5 in stage 3.

The general picture seems to be that at the beginning of the growing season the water is rich in nutrients and behaves rather

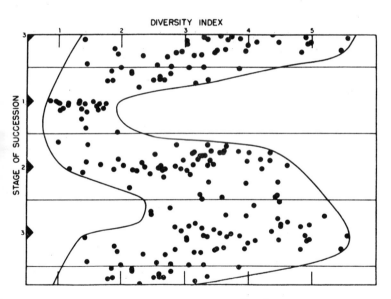

Figure 31.—Variation of diversity index ($d = \frac{S-1}{\log_e N}$) in relation to stage of succession in a number of spot samples taken in surface waters of the Gulf of Vigo, summer, 1955. From R. Margalef, Temporal succession and spatial heterogeneity in phytoplankton, in *Perspectives in Marine Biology,* ed. A. A. Buzzati-Traverso (1958), p. 338, fig. 5.

like an ordinary artificial culture medium containing only in-organic constituents—a point we have noted before (p. 59). The most rapidly growing species then becomes dominant. As a result of this growth, mineral nutrients are depleted, and organic by-products of metabolism begin to accumulate. Con-sequently, the species which now succeed are not the most rapidly growing but those which are best able to make use of the organic matter. In such a community we might expect inter-relations among species to be complex and the number of species consequently high. Increased stability of the water column and reduction of mixing at this stage result in reduced rates of growth and permit discrete clouds of organisms to be formed and to persist. Flagellates can remain in the surface waters, whereas diatoms sink so that the heterogeneity is vertical as well as horizontal. Some analogy with succession in terrestrial com-munities may be seen, as here, too, pioneer vegetation tends to consist of a few rapidly growing species, which are followed by a more complex and integrated community with more species. However, more definite biochemical information about the changes in dissolved organic matter and studies in culture of the nutritional requirements of the organisms concerned are needed to fill in the details of this picture.

REFERENCES
INDEX

REFERENCES

AACH, H. G. 1952. Über Wachstum und Zusammensetzung von *Chlorella pyrenoidosa* bei unterschiedlichen Lichtstärken und Nitratmengen. *Arch. Mikrobiol.* 17:213–246.

ABBOTT, B. C., AND BALLANTINE, D. 1957. The toxin from *Gymnodinium veneficum* Ballantine. *J. Mar. biol. Ass. U.K.* 36:169–189.

ALLEN, M. B. 1963a. Nitrogen fixing organisms in the sea. In *Symposium on Marine Microbiology*, ed. C. H. Oppenheimer; Springfield, Ill.; p. 85–92.

_____, FRENCH, C. S., AND BROWN, J. S. 1960. Native and extractable forms of chlorophyll in various algal groups. In *Comparative Biochemistry of Photoreactive Systems*, ed. M. B. Allen; New York and London; p. 33–52.

BAINBRIDGE, R. 1957. The size, shape and density of marine phytoplankton concentrations. *Biol. Rev.* 32:91–115.

BASSHAM, J. A., AND CALVIN, M. 1957. *The Path of Carbon in Photosynthesis.* Englewood Cliffs, N.J.

BELCHER, J. H., AND MILLER, J. D. A. 1960. Studies on the growth of Xanthophyceae in pure culture. IV. Nutritional types amongst the Xanthophyceae. *Arch. Mikrobiol.* 36:219–228.

BELSER, W. L. 1963. Bioassay of trace substances. In *The Sea*, vol. 2, ed. M. N. Hill; New York and London, p. 220–231.

BENTLEY, J. A. 1958. Role of plant hormones in algal metabolism and ecology. *Nature, Lond.* 181:1499–1502.

_____. 1960. Plant hormones in marine phytoplankton, zooplankton and seawater. *J. Mar. biol. Ass. U.K.* 39:433–444.

BERNARD, F. 1963. Density of flagellates and Myxophyceae in the heterotrophic layers related to environment. In *Symposium on Marine Microbiology*, ed. C. H. Oppenheimer; Springfield, Ill.; p. 215–228.

BRAARUD, T. 1962. Species distribution in marine phytoplankton. *J. Oceanogr. Soc. Japan*, 20th Anniversary Vol., p. 628–649.

CANTER, H. M., AND LUND, J. W. G. 1948. Studies on plankton parasites. I. Fluctuations in the numbers of *Asterionella formosa* Hass. in relation to fungal epidemics. *New Phytol. 47*:238–261.

Chu, S. P. 1942. The influence of the mineral composition of the medium on the growth of planktonic algae. I. Methods and culture media. *J. Ecol. 30*:284–325.

————. 1943. The influence of the mineral composition of the medium on the growth of planktonic algae. II. The influence of the concentration of inorganic nitrogen and phosphate phosphorus. *J. Ecol. 31*:109–148.

Collyer, D. M., and Fogg, G. E. 1955. Studies on fat accumulation by algae. *J. exp. Bot. 6*:256–275.

Cushing, D. H. 1959a. The seasonal variation in oceanic production as a problem in population dynamics. *J. Cons. int. Explor. Mer 24*:455–464.

————. 1959b. On the nature of production in the sea. *Fish. Invest., Lond., Ser. 2, 22*(6).

Danforth, W. F. 1962. Substrate assimilation and heterotrophy. In *Physiology and Biochemistry of Algae,* ed. R. A. Lewin; New York and London; p. 99–123.

Von Denffer, D. 1948. Über einen Wachstumshemmstoff in alternden Diatomeenkulturen. *Biol. Zbl. 67*:7–13.

Doty, M. S., and Oguri, M. 1957. Evidence for a photosynthetic daily periodicity. *Limnol. Oceanogr. 2*:37–40.

Droop, M. 1954. Conditions governing haematochrome formation and loss in the alga *Haematococcus pluvialis* Flotow. *Arch. Mikrobiol. 20*:391–397.

————. 1961a. Vitamin B_{12} and marine ecology: the response of *Monochrysis lutheri. J. Mar. biol. Ass. U.K. 41*:69–76.

————. 1961b. Some chemical considerations in the design of synthetic culture media for marine algae. *Botanica Marina 2*:231–246.

————. 1962a. On cultivating *Skeletonema costatum:* some problems. In *Beiträge zur Physiologie und Morphologie der Algen.* Vorträge aus dem Gesamtgebiet der Botanik, Deutschen Botanischen Gesellschaft, N.F. *1*:77–82.

————. 1962b. Organic micronutrients. In *Physiology and Biochemistry of Algae,* ed. R. A. Lewin; New York and London; p. 141–159.

Dugdale, R. C., Menzel, D. W., and Ryther, J. H. 1961. Nitrogen fixation in the Sargasso Sea. *Deep-Sea Res. 7*:297–300.

Dugdale, V. A., and Dugdale, R. C. 1962. Nitrogen metabolism in lakes. II. Role of nitrogen fixation in Sanctuary Lake, Pennsylvania. *Limnol. Oceanogr.* 7:170–177.

ERWIN, J., AND BLOCH, K. 1964. Biosynthesis of unsaturated fatty acids in micro-organisms. *Science* 143:1006–1012.

FOGG, G. E. 1941. The gas-vacuoles of the Myxophyceae (Cyanophyceae). *Biol. Rev.* 16:205–217.

————. 1944. Growth and heterocyst production in *Anabaena cylindrica* Lemm. *New Phytol.* 43:164–175.

————. 1949. Growth and heterocyst production in *Anabaena cylindrica* Lemm. II. In relation to carbon and nitrogen metabolism. *Ann. Bot., Lond., N.S.* 13:241–259.

————. 1952. The production of extracellular nitrogenous substances by a blue-green alga. *Proc. roy. Soc., B* 139:372–397.

————. 1956a. Photosynthesis and formation of fats in a diatom. *Ann. Bot., Lond., N.S.* 20:265–285.

————. 1956b. The comparative physiology and biochemistry of the blue-green algae. *Bact. Rev.* 20:148–165.

————. 1959. Nitrogen nutrition and metabolic patterns in algae. *Symp. Soc. exp. Biol.* 13:106–125.

————. 1962. Extracellular products. In *Physiology and Biochemistry of Algae*, ed. R. A. Lewin; New York and London; p. 475–489.

————. 1963. The role of algae in organic production in aquatic environments. *Brit. Phyc. Bull.* 2:195–205.

————, AND BELCHER, J. H. 1961. Physiological studies on a planktonic μ-alga. *Verh. int. Ver. Limnol.* 14:893–896

————, AND MILLBANK, J. W. 1960. The occurrence and metabolism of organic acids in algae. In *Encyclopedia of Plant Physiology*, ed. W. Ruhland; Berlin; 12(2):640–662.

————, AND NALEWAJKO, C. 1964. Glycollic acid as an extracellular product of phytoplankton. *Verh. int. Ver. Limnol.* 15:806–810.

————, SMITH, W. E. E., AND MILLER, J. D. A. 1959. An apparatus for the culture of algae under controlled conditions. *J. Biochem. Microbiol. Tech. Engng* 1:59–76.

————, AND THAN-TUN. 1960. Interrelations of photosynthesis and assimilation of elementary nitrogen in a blue-green alga. *Proc. roy. Soc., B* 153:111–127.

————, AND WESTLAKE, D. F. 1955. The importance of extracellular products of algae in freshwater. *Verh. int. Ver. Limnol.* 12:219–232.

FUJIMOTO, Y., IWAMOTO, H., KATO, A. AND YAMADA, K. 1956. Studies on the growth of *Chlorella* by continuous cultivation. *Bull. agric.*

chem. Soc. Japan 20:13–18.

GERLOFF, G. C., FITZGERALD, G. P., AND SKOOG, F. 1950. The isolation, purification, and nutrient solution requirements of blue-green algae. In *Symposium on the culturing of algae.* Charles F. Kettering Foundation, Dayton, Ohio; p. 27–44.

————, AND SKOOG, F. 1954. Cell contents of nitrogen and phosphorus as a measure of their availability for growth of *Microcystis aeruginosa. Ecology* 35:348–353.

————, AND ————. 1957. Nitrogen as a limiting factor for the growth of *Microcystis aeruginosa* in southern Wisconsin lakes. *Ecology* 38:556–561.

GOLDBERG, E. D. 1963. The oceans as a chemical system. In *The Sea,* vol. 2, ed. M. N. Hill; New York and London; p. 3–25.

GOLDMAN, C. R. 1960. Molybdenum as a factor limiting primary productivity in Castle Lake, California. *Science* 132:1016–1017.

————, 1961. Primary productivity and limiting factors in Brooks Lake, Alaska. *Verh. int. Ver. Limnol.* 14:120–124.

GORHAM, E. 1957. The chemical composition of some waters from lowland lakes in Shropshire, England. *Tellus* 9:174–179.

GRAN, H. H., AND BRAARUD, T. 1935. A quantitative study of the phytoplankton in the Bay of Fundy and the Gulf of Maine (including observations on hydrography, chemistry and turbidity). *J. biol. Bd. Can.* 1:279–467.

GROSS, F., AND ZEUTHEN, E. 1948. The buoyancy of plankton diatoms: a problem of cell physiology. *Proc. roy. Soc., B* 135:382–389.

HAECKEL, E. 1890. *Plankton-Studien.* Jena.

HARDER, R. 1917. Ernährungsphysiologische Untersuchungen an Cyanophyceen, hauptsächlich dem endophytischen *Nostoc punctiforme. Z. Bot.* 9:145–242.

HARVEY, H. W. 1945. *Recent advances in the chemistry and biology of sea water.* Cambridge.

HASE, E. 1962. Cell division. In *Physiology and Biochemistry of Algae,* ed. R. A. Lewin; New York and London; p. 617–624.

HINSHELWOOD, C. N. 1946. *The chemical kinetics of the bacterial cell.* Oxford.

HOLMES, R. W., AND ANDERSON, G. C. 1963. Size fractionation of C^{14}-labeled natural phytoplankton. In *Symposium on Marine Microbiology,* ed. C. H. Oppenheimer; Springfield, Ill.; p. 241–250.

HOLM-HANSEN, O., NISHIDA, K., MOSES, V., AND CALVIN, M. 1959. Effects of mineral salts on short-term incorporation of carbon dioxide in *Chlorella. J. exp. Bot.* 10:109–124.

Hoogenhout, H. 1963. Synchronous cultures of algae. *Phycologia* 2:135–147.

Hughes, J. C., and Lund, J. W. G. 1962. The rate of growth of *Asterionella formosa* Hass. in relation to its ecology. *Arch. Mikrobiol.* 42:117–129.

Hutchens, J. O. 1948. Growth of *Chilomonas paramecium* in mass cultures. *J. cell. comp. Physiol.* 32:105–116.

Hutchinson, G. E. 1944. Limnological studies in Connecticut. VII. A critical examination of the supposed relationship between phytoplankton periodicity and chemical changes in lake waters. *Ecology* 25:3–26.

———. 1957. *A Treatise on Limnology,* vol. 1; New York and London.

Hutner, S. H., Baker, H., Aaronson, S., Nathan, H. A., Rodriguez, E., Lockwood, S., Sanders, M., and Peterson, R. A. 1957. Growing *Ochromonas malhamensis* above 35° C. *J. Protozool.* 4:259–269.

Jakob, H. 1961. *Compatibilités, antagonismes et antibioses entre quelques algues du sol.* Thèse no. 4485. Fac. Sciences, Univ. de Paris.

Jitts, H. R., McAllister, C. D., Stephens, K., and Strickland, J. D. H. 1964. The cell division rates of some marine phytoplankters as a function of light and temperature. *J. Fish. Res. Bd Can.* 21:139–157.

Johnson, M. W., and Brinton, E. 1963. Biological species, watermasses and currents. In *The Sea,* vol. 2, ed. M. N. Hill; New York and London; p. 381–414.

Johnston, R. 1963a. Antimetabolites as an aid to the study of phytoplankton nutrition. *J. Mar. biol. Ass. U.K.* 43:409–425.

———. 1963b. Sea water, the natural medium of phytoplankton I. General features. *J. Mar. biol. Ass. U.K.* 43:427–456.

Jørgensen, E. G. 1956. Growth inhibiting substances formed by algae. *Physiol. Plant.* 9:712–726.

———. 1957. Diatom periodicity and silicon assimilation. *Dansk bot. Ark.* 18(1):1–54.

———. 1962. Antibiotic substances from cells and culture solutions of unicellular algae with special references to some chlorophyll derivatives. *Physiol. Plant.* 15:530–545.

Kain, J. M., and Fogg, G. E. 1958. Studies on the growth of marine phytoplankton. I. *Asterionella japonica* Gran. *J. Mar. biol. Ass. U.K.* 37:397–413.

———, and ———. 1960. Studies on the growth of marine

phytoplankton. III. *Prorocentrum micans* Ehrenberg. *J. Mar. biol. Ass. U.K.* 39:33–50.

KETCHUM, B. H. 1954. Mineral nutrition of phytoplankton. *Annu. Rev. Pl. Physiol.* 5:55–74.

KRATZ, W. A., AND MYERS, J. 1955. Nutrition and growth of several blue-green algae. *Amer. J. Bot.* 42:282–287.

KRAUSS, R. W. 1953. Inorganic nutrition of algae. In *Algal culture from laboratory to pilot plant*, ed. J. S. Burlew; Carnegie Institution of Washington Publication no. 600; p. 85–102.

KUMAR, H. D. 1964. Streptomycin- and penicillin-induced inhibition of growth and pigment production in blue-green algae and production of strains of *Anacystis nidulans* resistant to these antibiotics. *J. exp. Bot.* 15:232–250.

KUSNEZOW, S. I. 1959. *Die Rolle der Mikroorganismen im Stoffkreislauf der Seen.* Berlin.

LEFÈVRE, M., AND JAKOB, H. 1949. Sur quelques propriétés des substances actives tirées des cultures d'algues d'eau douce. *C. R. Acad. Sci., Paris* 229:234–236.

LEWIN, J. C. 1963. Heterotrophy in marine diatoms. In *Symposium on Marine Microbiology*, ed. C. H. Oppenheimer; Springfield, Ill.; p. 229–235.

LEWIN, R. A. 1958. Vitamin-bezonoj de algoj. In *Sciencaj Studoj*, ed. P. Neergaard; Copenhagen; p. 187–192.

————. 1962. (Editor) *Physiology and Biochemistry of Algae.* New York and London.

LORENZEN, H. 1959. Die photosynthetische Sauerstoffproduktion wachsender *Chlorella* bei langfristig intermittierender Belichtung. *Flora, Jena* 147:382–404.

LUND, J. W. G. 1949. Studies on *Asterionella*. I. The origin and nature of the cells producing seasonal maxima. *J. Ecol.* 37:389–419.

————. 1950. Studies on *Asterionella formosa* Hass. II. Nutrient depletion and the spring maximum. *J. Ecol.* 38:1–14, 15–35.

————. 1954. The seasonal cycle of the plankton diatom, *Melosira italica* (Ehr.) Kütz. subsp. *subarctica* O. Müll. *J. Ecol.* 42:151–179.

————. 1955. Further observations on the seasonal cycle of *Melosira italica* (Ehr.) Kütz. subsp. *subarctica* O. Müll. *J. Ecol.* 43:90–102.

————. 1959. Buoyancy in relation to the ecology of the freshwater phytoplankton. *Brit. Phyc. Bull.* 1(7):1–17.

————. 1961. The periodicity of μ-algae in three English lakes.

Verh. int. Ver. Limnol. 14:147–154.

————, MACKERETH, F. J. H., AND MORTIMER, C. H. 1963. Changes in depth and time of certain chemical and physical conditions and of the standing crop of *Asterionella formosa* Hass. in the north basin of Windermere in 1947. *Phil. Trans. roy. Soc.,* B *246*: 255–290.

————, AND TALLING, J. F. 1957. Botanical limnological methods with special reference to the algae. *Bot. Rev. 23*:489–583.

MAALØE, O. 1962. Synchronous growth. In *The Bacteria. Vol. 4. The Physiology of Growth,* ed. I. C. Gunsalus and R. Y. Stanier; New York and London; 1–32.

MACKERETH, F. J. 1953. Phosphorus utilization by *Asterionella formosa* Hass. *J. exp. Bot. 4*:296–313.

MADDUX, W. S., AND JONES, R. F. 1964. Some interactions of temperature, light intensity, and nutrient concentration during the continuous culture of *Nitzschia closterium* and *Tetraselmis* sp. *Limnol. Oceanogr. 9*:79–86.

MARGALEF, R. 1958. Temporal succession and spatial heterogeneity in phytoplankton. In *Perspectives in Marine Biology,* ed. A. A. Buzzati-Traverso; Berkeley and Los Angeles; p. 323–349.

MENZEL, D. W., AND SPAETH, J. P. 1962. Occurrence of vitamin B_{12} in the Sargasso Sea. *Limnol. Oceanogr. 7*:151–154.

MILLER, J. D. A. 1957. Studies on *Monodus subterraneus* in pure culture. Thesis for Ph.D., University of London.

————, AND FOGG, G. E. 1957. Studies on the growth of Xanthophyceae in pure culture. I. The mineral nutrition of *Monodus subterraneus* Petersen. *Arch. Mikrobiol. 28*:1–17.

————, AND ————. 1958. Studies on the growth of Xanthophyceae in pure culture. II. The relations of *Monodus subterraneus* to organic substances. *Arch. Mikrobiol. 30*:1–16.

MONOD, J. 1950. La technique de culture continue; théorie et applications. *Ann. inst. Pasteur 79*:390–401.

MUNK, W. H., AND RILEY, G. A. 1952. Absorption of nutrients by aquatic plants. *J. Mar. Res. 11*:215–240.

MYERS, J. 1946a. Culture conditions and the development of the photosynthetic mechanism. III. Influence of light intensity on cellular characteristics of *Chlorella. J. gen. Physiol. 29*:419–427.

————. 1946b. Culture conditions and the development of the photosynthetic mechanism. IV. Influence of light intensity on photosynthetic characteristics of *Chlorella. J. gen. Physiol. 29*:429–440.

————. 1947. Culture conditions and the development of the

photosynthetic mechanism. V. Influence of the composition of the nutrient medium. *Plant Physiol. 22*:590–597.

————. 1949. The pattern of photosynthesis in *Chlorella*. In *Photosynthesis in Plants,* ed. J. Franck and W. E. Loomis; Ames, Iowa; p. 349–364.

————. 1951. Physiology of the Algae. *Annu. Rev. Microbiol. 5*: 157–180.

————. 1953. Growth characteristics of algae in relation to the problems of mass culture. In *Algal Culture from Laboratory to Pilot Plant,* ed. J. S. Burlew; Carnegie Institution of Washington Publication no. 600; p. 37–54.

————. 1962. Laboratory Cultures. In *Physiology and Biochemistry of Algae,* ed. R. A. Lewin; New York and London; p. 603–615.

————, AND CLARK, L. B. 1944. Culture conditions and the development of the photosynthetic mechanism. II. An apparatus for the continuous culture of *Chlorella. J. gen. Physiol. 28*:103–112.

————, AND GRAHAM, J.-R. 1956. The role of photosynthesis in the physiology of *Ochromonas. J. cell. comp. Physiol. 47*:397–414.

————, AND ————. 1959. On the mass culture of algae. II. Yield as a function of cell concentration under continuous sunlight irradiance. *Plant Physiol. 34*:345–352.

————, PHILLIPS, J. N. AND GRAHAM, J.-R. 1951. On the mass culture of algae. *Plant Physiol. 26*:539–548.

NALEWAJKO, C., CHOWDHURI, N., AND FOGG, G. E. 1963. Excretion of glycollic acid and the growth of a planktonic *Chlorella*. In *Studies on Microalgae and Photosynthetic Bacteria;* Tokyo; p. 171–183.

NAUWERCK, A. 1963. Die Beziehungen zwischen Zooplankton und Phytoplankton im See Erken. *Symb. bot. upsaliens. 17*(5):1–163.

NIHEI, T., SASA, T., MIYACHI, S., SUZUKI, K., AND TAMIYA, H. 1954. Change of photosynthetic activity of *Chlorella* cells during the course of their normal life cycle. *Arch. Mikrobiol. 21*:155–164.

NORDLI, E. 1957. Experimental studies on the ecology of *Ceratia*. *Acta oecol. scand. 8*:200–265.

NOVICK, A., AND SZILARD, L. 1950. Description of the chemostat. *Science 112*:715–716.

OHLE, W. 1958. Diurnal production and destruction rates of phytoplankton in lakes. *Rapp. Proc.-Verb. Cons. int. Explor. Mer 144*: 129–131.

————. 1961. Tagesrhythmen der Photosynthese von Planktonbiocoenosen. *Verh. int. Ver. Limnol. 14*:113–119.

VAN OORSCHOT, J. L. P. 1955. Conversion of light energy in algal cultures. *Meded. LandbHoogesch., Wageningen* 55:225–276.

OTSUKA, H. 1961. Changes of lipid and carbohydrate contents in *Chlorella* cells during the sulfur starvation, as studied by the technique of synchronous culture. *J. gen. appl. Microbiol., Tokyo* 7:72–77.

PAASCHE, E. 1960a. On the relationship between primary production and standing stock of phytoplankton. *J. Cons. int. Explor. Mer* 26:33–48.

————. 1960b. Phytoplankton distribution in the Norwegian Sea in June, 1954, related to hydrography and compared with primary production data. *Fiskeridir. Skr. Havundersøk.* 12(11):1–77.

PAREDES, J. F. 1962. On an occurrence of red waters in the coast of Angola. *Mem. Jta Invest. Ultram.* 2nd. ser. no. 33, 89–114.

PARSONS, T. R., STEPHENS, K., AND STRICKLAND, J. D. H. 1961. On the chemical composition of eleven species of marine phytoplankters. *J. Fish. Res. Bd Can.* 18:1001–1016.

————, AND STRICKLAND, J. D. H. 1962. On the production of particulate organic carbon by heterotrophic processes in sea water. *Deep-Sea Res.* 8:211–222.

PEARSALL, W. H. 1932. Phytoplankton in the English Lakes. 2. The composition of the phytoplankton in relation to dissolved substances. *J. Ecol.* 20:241–262.

————, AND BENGRY, R. P. 1940. The growth of *Chlorella* in darkness and in glucose solution. *Ann. Bot., Lond., N.S.* 4:365–377.

PHILLIPS, J. N., JR., AND MYERS, J. 1954. Measurement of algal growth under controlled steady-state conditions. *Plant Physiol.* 29:148–152.

PINTNER, I. J., AND PROVASOLI, L. 1963. Nutritional characteristics of some chrysomonads. In *Symposium on Marine Microbiology*, ed. C. H. Oppenheimer; Springfield, Ill.; p. 114–121.

PIRSON, A. 1957. Induced periodicity of photosynthesis and respiration in *Hydrodictyon*. In *Research in Photosynthesis*, ed. H. Gaffron et al.; New York and London; p. 490–499.

————, AND LORENZEN, H. 1958. Ein endogener Zeitfaktor bei der Teilung von *Chlorella*. *Z. Bot.* 46:53–66.

PRATT, R. 1943. Studies on *Chlorella vulgaris*. VI. Retardation of photosynthesis by a growth-inhibiting substance from *Chlorella vulgaris*. *Amer. J. Bot.* 30:32–33.

————, AND FONG, J. 1940. Studies on *Chlorella vulgaris*. II. Further evidence that *Chlorella* cells form a growth-inhibiting substance. *Amer. J. Bot.* 27:431–436.

PRINGSHEIM, E. G. 1946. *Pure Cultures of Algae.* Cambridge.

————, AND WIESSNER, W. 1961. Ernährung und Stoffwechsel von *Chlamydobotrys* (Volvocales). *Arch. Mikrobiol.* 40:231–246.

PROCTOR, V. W. 1957. Studies of algal antibiosis using *Haematococcus* and *Chlamydomonas. Limnol. Oceanogr.* 2:125–139.

PROVASOLI, L. 1963. Organic regulation of phytoplankton fertility. In *The Sea*, vol. 2, ed. M. N. Hill; New York and London; p. 165–219.

————, MCLAUGHLIN, J. J. A., AND DROOP, M. R. 1957. The development of artificial media for marine algae. *Arch. Mikrobiol.* 25:392–428.

PROWSE, G. A., AND TALLING, J. F. 1958. The seasonal growth and succession of plankton algae in the White Nile. *Limnol. Oceanogr.* 3:222–238.

RILEY, G. A. 1963. Theory of food-chain relations in the ocean. In *The Sea*, vol. 2, ed. M. N. Hill; New York and London; p. 438–463.

————. In the press. (Editor) *Marine Biology II. Second International Interdisciplinary Conference on Marine Biology;* Washington, D.C.

ROACH, B. M. BRISTOL. 1928. On the influence of light and of glucose on the growth of a soil alga. *Ann. Bot., Lond.* 42:317–345.

RODHE, W. 1948. Environmental requirements of fresh-water plankton algae. *Symb. bot. upsaliens.* 101:1–149.

————. 1955. Can plankton production proceed during winter darkness in sub-arctic lakes? *Verh. int. Ver. Limnol.* 12:117–122.

————. 1958. The primary production in lakes: some results and restrictions of the ^{14}C method. *Rapp. Proc.-Verb. Cons. int. Explor. Mer* 144:122–128.

————, VOLLENWEIDER, R. A., AND NAUWERCK, A. 1958. The primary production and standing crop of phytoplankton. In *Perspectives in Marine Biology*, ed. A. A. Buzzati-Traverso; Berkeley and Los Angeles; p. 299–322.

RUTTNER, F. 1953. *Fundamentals of Limnology;* Toronto.

RYTHER, J. H. 1955. Ecology of autotrophic marine dinoflagellates with reference to red water conditions. In *The Luminescence of Biological Systems*, ed. F. H. Johnson; Washington, D.C.; p. 387–414.

————. 1963. Geographic variations in productivity. In *The Sea*, vol. 2, ed. M. N. Hill; New York and London; p. 347–380.

————, AND GUILLARD, R. R. L. 1959. Enrichment experiments as a means of studying nutrients limiting to phytoplankton production. *Deep-Sea Res. 6:65–69.*

————, AND MENZEL, D. W. 1959. Light adaptation by marine phytoplankton. *Limnol. Oceanogr. 4:492–497.*

————, AND YENTSCH, C. S. 1957. The estimation of phytoplankton production in the ocean from chlorophyll and light data. *Limnol. Oceanogr. 2:281–286.*

SHIMADA, B. M. 1958. Diurnal fluctuation in photosynthetic rate and chlorophyll A content of phytoplankton from eastern Pacific waters. *Limnol. Oceanogr. 3:336–339.*

SMAYDA, T. J. 1963. Succession of phytoplankton, and the ocean as an holocoenotic environment. In *Symposium on Marine Microbiology,* ed. C. H. Oppenheimer; Springfield, Ill.; p. 260–274.

SOROKIN, C. 1957. Changes in photosynthetic activity in the course of cell development in *Chlorella. Physiol. Plant. 10:659–666.*

————. 1959. Tabular comparative data for the low- and high-temperature strains of *Chlorella. Nature, Lond. 184:613–614.*

SPEKTOROV, K. S., AND LIN'KOVA, E. A. 1962. A new simple method of synchronizing *Chlorella cultures. C.R. Acad. Sci. U.R.S.S. 147:* 967–969.

SPENCER, C. P. 1954. Studies on the culture of a marine diatom. *J. Mar. biol. Ass. U.K. 33:265–290.*

SPOEHR, H. A., AND MILNER, H. W. 1949. The chemical composition of *Chlorella;* effect of environmental conditions. *Plant Physiol. 24:120–149.*

STAUB, R. 1961. Ernährungsphysiologisch-autökologische Untersuchungen an der planktischen Blaualge *Oscillatoria rubescens* DC. *Schweiz. Z. Hydrol. 23:82–198a.*

STEELE, J. H. 1958. *Plant production in the northern North Sea.* Scottish Home Department, Marine Research no. 7; Edinburgh.

————. 1962. Environmental control of photosynthesis in the sea. *Limnol. Oceanogr. 7:137–150.*

————. 1963. In *Marine Biology I. First International Interdisciplinary Conference on Marine Biology,* ed. G. A. Riley; Washington, D.C.; p. 50.

————, AND BAIRD, I. E. 1961. Relations between primary production, chlorophyll and particulate carbon. *Limnol. Oceanogr. 6:68–78.*

————, AND ————. 1962. Carbon-chlorophyll relations in cultures. *Limnol. Oceanogr. 7:101–102.*

————, AND YENTSCH, C. S. 1960. The vertical distribution of

chlorophyll. *J. Mar. biol. Ass. U.K.* 39:217–226.

STEEMANN NIELSEN, E. 1955. The production of organic matter by the phytoplankton in a Danish lake receiving extraordinarily great amounts of nutrient salts. *Hydrobiologia* 7:68–74.

————, 1960. Productivity of the oceans. *Annu. Rev. Pl. Physiol.* 11:341–362.

————. 1963. Productivity, definition and measurement. In *The Sea*, vol. 2, ed. M. N. Hill; New York and London; 129–164.

————. In the press. In *Marine Biology II. Second International Interdisciplinary Conference on Marine Biology*, ed. G. A. Riley; Washington, D.C.

————, AND HANSEN, V. G. 1959. Light adaptation in marine phytoplankton populations and its interrelation with temperature. *Physiol. Plant.* 12:353–370.

————, ————, AND JØRGENSEN, E. G. 1962. The adaptation to different light intensities in *Chlorella vulgaris* and the time dependence on transfer to a new light intensity. *Physiol. Plant.* 15:505–517.

————, AND JØRGENSEN, E. G. 1962. The physiological background for using chlorophyll measurements in hydrobiology and a theory explaining daily variations in chlorophyll concentration. *Arch. Hydrobiol.* 58:349–357.

STEWART, W. D. P. 1962. Fixation of elemental nitrogen by marine blue-green algae. *Ann. Bot., Lond., N.S.* 26:439–447.

STRICKLAND, J. D. H. 1960. Measuring the production of marine phytoplankton. *Fish. Res. Bd Can.*, Bulletin no. 122; Ottawa.

SVERDRUP, H. U. 1953. On conditions for the vernal blooming of phytoplankton. *J. Cons. int. Explor. Mer* 18:287–295.

————, JOHNSON, M. W., AND FLEMING, R. H. 1942. *The Oceans;* Englewood Cliffs, N.J.

SWEENEY, B. M., AND HASTINGS, J. W. 1962. Rhythms. In *Physiology and Biochemistry of Algae*, ed. R. A. Lewin. New York and London, p. 687–700.

TALLING, J. F. 1957a. Diurnal changes of stratification and photosynthesis in some tropical African waters. *Proc. roy. Soc., B 147:* 57–83.

————. 1957b. The growth of two plankton diatoms in mixed cultures. *Physiol. Plant.* 10:215–223.

————. 1960a. Comparative laboratory and field studies of photosynthesis by a marine planktonic diatom. *Limnol. Oceanogr.* 5:62–77.

————. 1960b. Self-shading effects in natural populations of a planktonic diatom. *Wetter und Leben 12*:235–242.

—————. 1961*a*. Photosynthesis under natural conditions. *Annu. Rev. Pl. Physiol. 12*:133–154.

—————. 1961*b*. Report on limnological work during a visit to EAFFRO between August 1960, and September 1961. *East African Freshwater Fishery Research Organization, Annual Report 1961,* 40–42.

—————. 1962. Freshwater algae. In *Physiology and Biochemistry of Algae,* ed. R. A. Lewin; New York and London; p. 743–757.

TAMIYA, H. 1963. Cell differentiation in *Chlorella. Symp. Soc. exp. Biol. 17*:188–214.

—————, IWAMURA, T., SHIBATA, K., HASE, E., AND NIHEI, T. 1953. Correlation between photosynthesis and light-independent metabolism in the growth of *Chlorella. Biochim. biophys. Acta 12*:23–40.

TOLBERT, N. E., AND ZILL, L. P. 1956. Excretion of glycolic acid by algae during photosynthesis. *J. biol. Chem. 222*:895–906.

VERDUIN, J. 1951. A comparison of phytoplankton data obtained by a mobile sampling method with those obtained from a single station. *Amer. J. Bot. 38*:5–11.

—————. 1956. Energy fixation and utilization by natural communities in western Lake Erie. *Ecology 37*:40–49.

WASSINK, E. C. 1954. Problems in the mass cultivation of photoautotrophic micro-organisms. *Symp. Soc. gen. Microbiol. 4*:247–270.

WATT, W. D., AND HAYES, F. R. 1963. Tracer study of the phosphorus cycle in sea water. *Limnol. Oceanogr. 8*:276–285.

WHITTINGHAM, C. P., AND PRITCHARD, G. G. 1963. The production of glycollate during photosynthesis in *Chlorella. Proc. roy. Soc., B 157*:366–380.

WILLIAMS, A. E., AND BURRIS, R. H. 1952. Nitrogen fixation by blue-green algae and their nitrogenous composition. *Amer. J. Bot. 39*:340–342.

WILSON, D. P., AND ARMSTRONG, F. A. J. 1958. Biological differences between sea waters: experiments in 1954 and 1955. *J. Mar. biol. Ass. U.K. 37*:331–348.

WINOKUR, M. 1948. Growth relationships of *Chlorella* species. *Amer. J. Bot. 35*:118–129.

WRIGHT, J. C. 1960. The limnology of Canyon Ferry Reservoir: III. Some observations on the density dependence of photosynthesis and its cause. *Limnol. Oceanogr. 5*:356–361.

YENTSCH, C. S., AND RYTHER, J. H. 1957. Short-term variations in phytoplankton chlorophyll and their significance. *Limnol. Oceanogr.* 2:140–142.

ZAVARZINA, N. B. 1959. On some factors inhibiting the development of *Scenedesmus quadricauda. Trud. vsesoyuz. gidrobiol. Obshch.* 9:195–205.

ZOBELL, C. E. 1946. *Marine Microbiology.* Waltham, Mass.

INDEX